MW00635595

NATIONAL
MATH + SCIENCE
INITIATIVE

MATHEMATICS

Module 3

Graphical Displays
& Distributions

2013 EDITION

ISBN 978-1-935167-15-0

Grateful acknowledgment is given authors, publishers, and agents for permission to reprint copyrighted material. Every effort has been made to determine copyright owners. In case of any omission, the publisher will be pleased to make suitable acknowledgments in future editions.

Published by:

National Math + Science Initiative
8350 North Central Expressway
Suite M-2200
Dallas, TX 75206

www.nms.org

Graphical Displays & Distributions

CONTENTS

Belief Statements i

Middle Grades Learner Outcomes ii

High School Learner Outcomes iii

Lessons and Assessments 1

    Graphical Displays & Distributions
    Content Progression Chart 3

    Graphical Displays & Distributions
    Concept Development Chart. 4

    Measures of Central Tendency and Variability 5

    Histograms 21

    Box-and-Whisker Plots. 37

    Linear Functions, Transformations,
    and Graphical Displays. 49

    Describing Distributions: Standard Deviation 67

    Geometry and Graphical Displays 81

    Empirical Rule and Normal Distributions 93

    Analyzing Trigonometric Functions
    Using Graphical Displays 105

    Multiple Choice Quizzes. 117

    Free Response Questions 131

Appendix. A1

    Standards for Mathematical Practice A3

    Additional Graphs and Materials A11

    Graphical Organizer A19

This page is intentionally left blank.

www.nms.org

National Math + Science

Belief Statements

Accomplished, dynamic teachers are knowledgeable in their content and confident in their abilities to prepare students for higher education. They create classrooms in which students:

- engage intellectually to develop conceptual understanding

- generate their own ideas, questions, and propositions

- interact collegially with one another to solve problems

- employ appropriate resources for inquiry-based learning

Our teacher training program offers meaningful support to teachers as they construct these effective classrooms. Through tested content materials and research-based instructional strategies, our program enables and encourages them to:

- choose significant and worthwhile content and connect it to other knowledge

- use appropriate questioning strategies to develop conceptual understanding

- clarify to students the importance of abstract concepts and "big questions"

- use formative assessments to improve instruction and achieve higher goals

- guarantee equitable access for all students to information and achievement

Graphical Displays & Distributions
Middle Grades

MODULE DESCRIPTION

Middle school teachers examine how concepts involving graphical displays and distributions progress from sixth grade to statistics. Participants examine classroom-ready middle grades lessons which require students to construct, compare, analyze, and interpret box-and-whisker plots, line plots (dotplots), histograms, and stem-and-leaf plots. Each lesson involves creating, by hand or with a graphing calculator, appropriate graphical displays based on real-world data. Graphs are analyzed by investigating measures of central tendency, variability, and shape. In addition, teachers work through and discuss a lesson for Geometry or Math 2 in which students observe variability in data collected using measurement. Algebra 1 or Math 1 lessons connecting transformations to graphical displays and introducing standard deviation as a measure of variability are also explored in the training.

LEARNER OUTCOMES

Participants will:

- Compare expectations for students from sixth grade math through pre-calculus on the topics of graphical displays and distributions to increase vertical alignment.

- Apply deeper content-based knowledge to increase instructional rigor in order to prepare students for high school math courses leading to college-level statistics in an AP class or university setting.

  - Construct, compare, analyze, and interpret histograms, box-and-whisker plots, line plots (dotplots), and stem-and-leaf plots.

  - Analyze graphs using measures of central tendency, variability, and shape.

  - Describe distributions using mean, mean absolute deviation, and standard deviation.

  - Identify the effects of measurement inaccuracies on the distribution of area and volume calculations.

  - Construct box-and-whisker plots of randomly selected function values over a limited domain and analyze the effects of transformations on the distribution of those function values.

  - Connect graphical displays of randomly selected function values over a limited domain to the behavior of the function over that limited domain.

  - Demonstrate graphing calculator skills used in creating graphical displays and calculating distributions.

- Identify instructional strategies that teachers can use to assist students in developing the habits of mind that are required for college and career readiness.

Graphical Displays & Distributions
High School

MODULE DESCRIPTION

High school teachers examine how concepts involving graphical displays and distributions progress from sixth grade to statistics. Training begins with an introductory activity that provides a comprehensive overview of all of the skills included in the middle grades lessons. Teachers work through and discuss classroom-ready lessons in which students observe variability in data collected using measurement, connect transformations to graphical displays, compute standard deviation, and use the Empirical rule and z-scores to estimate population percentages for normal distributions.

LEARNER OUTCOMES

Participants will:

- Compare expectations for students from sixth grade math through pre-calculus on the topics of graphical displays and distributions to increase vertical alignment.

- Apply deeper content-based knowledge to increase instructional rigor in order to prepare students for college-level statistics in an AP class or university setting.

  o Construct, compare, analyze, and interpret histograms, box-and-whisker plots, line plots (dotplots), and stem-and-leaf plots.

  o Analyze graphs using measures of central tendency, variability, and shape.

  o Describe distributions using mean and standard deviation.

  o Apply the Empirical Rule and z-scores to estimate population percentages for normal distributions.

  o Identify the effects of measurement inaccuracies on the distribution of area and volume calculations.

  o Construct box-and-whisker plots of randomly selected function values over a limited domain and analyze the effects of transformations on the distribution of those function values.

  o Connect graphical displays of randomly selected function values over a limited domain to the behavior of the function over that limited domain.

  o Demonstrate graphing calculator skills used in creating graphical displays and calculating distributions.

- Identify instructional strategies that teachers can use to assist students in developing the habits of mind that are required for college and career readiness.

Advanced Placement and AP* are registered trademarks of the College Entrance Examination Board. The College Board was not involved in the production of this product.*

NATIONAL
MATH + SCIENCE
INITIATIVE

This page is intentionally left blank.

www.nms.org

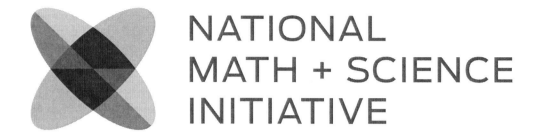

NATIONAL
MATH + SCIENCE
INITIATIVE

Graphical Displays
& Distributions

LESSONS AND ASSESSMENTS

NATIONAL
MATH + SCIENCE
INITIATIVE

This page is intentionally left blank.

www.nms.org

Graphical Displays & Distributions Content Progression Chart

6th Grade	7th Grade	Algebra 1	Geometry	Algebra 2	Pre-Calculus
Create, interpret, and compare dotplots (line plots), stemplots, and bar graphs.	Create, interpret, and compare dotplots (line plots), stemplots, bar graphs, histograms, and boxplots.	Create, interpret, and compare dotplots (line plots), stemplots, bar graphs, histograms, and boxplots.	Create, interpret, and compare dotplots (line plots), stemplots, bar graphs, histograms, and boxplots.	Create, interpret, and compare dotplots (line plots), stemplots, bar graphs, histograms, and boxplots.	Create, interpret, and compare dotplots (line plots), stemplots, bar graphs, histograms, and boxplots.
Calculate the mean, median, mode, range, and mean absolute deviation from tabular or graphical data or data presented in paragraph form.	Calculate the mean, median, mode, range, and mean absolute deviation from tabular or graphical data or data presented in paragraph form.	Calculate the mean, median, mode, range, and standard deviation from tabular or graphical data or data presented in paragraph form.	Calculate the mean, median, mode, range, and standard deviation from tabular or graphical data or data presented in paragraph form.	Calculate the mean, median, mode, range, and standard deviation from tabular or graphical data or data presented in paragraph form.	Calculate the mean, median, mode, range, and standard deviation from tabular or graphical data or data presented in paragraph form.
Determine the effect on the mean, median, mode, range, and mean absolute deviation of making a change in the data and determine changes that do not affect the mean and/or median.	Determine the effect on the mean, median, mode, range, and mean absolute deviation of making a change in the data and determine changes that do not affect the mean and/or median.	Determine the effect on the mean, median, mode, range, and standard deviation of making a change in the data and determine changes that do not affect the mean and/or median.	Determine the effect on the mean, median, mode, range, and standard deviation of making a change in the data and determine changes that do not affect the mean and/or median.	Determine the effect on the mean, median, mode, range, and standard deviation of making a change in the data and determine changes that do not affect the mean and/or median.	Determine the effect on the mean, median, mode, range, and standard deviation of making a change in the data and determine changes that do not affect the mean and/or median.
			Determine population percentages and probability for normal distributions using the empirical rule, tables, and technology.	Determine population percentages and probability for normal distributions using the empirical rule, tables, and technology.	Determine population percentages and probability for normal distributions using the empirical rule, tables, and technology.

Graphical Displays & Distributions Concept Development Chart

Grade 6

Jacey's classmates recorded the number of hours, rounded to the nearest five hours, they spent on the internet last week. Jacey made a dotplot (line plot) with the data.

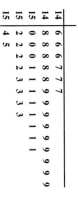

Hours Jacey's Classmates
Spent on the Internet

Does the dotplot of all the hours appear to have a symmetrical shape? Explain.

Based on the distribution of hours spent on the internet, what is the relationship between the mean and median of the data? Justify your answer.

Geometry

Mrs. Lewis gave her students a geometric shape to measure and told them to calculate the area to the nearest tenth. Due to variability in measurement, the area calculations differ. A stemplot is given that shows the distribution of the areas.

Area Data

```
14 | 6 6 6 7 7 7
14 | 8 8 8 8 8 9 9 9 9 9 9 9
15 | 0 0 0 1 1 1 1 1 1 1 1
15 | 2 2 2 2 2 3 3 3 3
15 | 4 5
```

Key: 15|4 means 15.4 square units

What are the dimensions of at least 3 different geometric shapes that Mrs. Lewis could have given her students to obtain this distribution of areas?

Grade 7

Craig is interested in the size of fish caught in a lake near his home. He collected the weights of fish caught over 5 pounds for the past six months. The distribution of fish weights over 5 pounds is shown in the histogram.

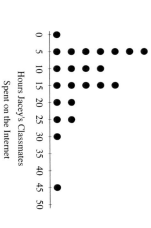

Weights of Fish greater than 5 pounds

Frequency

Fish Weight (lbs)

According to the histogram, how many fish have been caught that weigh at least 7 pounds?

Which bin contains the median weight of fish caught?

Algebra 2

Consider the distribution of offensive lineman in a professional football league. The mean weight for offensive linemen in the league is 295.3 lbs with a standard deviation of 4.2 lbs, and the distribution is approximately normal.

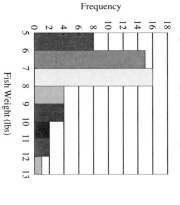

Draw vertical lines on the sketch of the distribution showing the mean and standard deviations out to ± 3 standard deviations. Label the percent of the population within 1, 2, and 3 standard deviations

What percent of offensive linemen are between 286.9 lbs and 299.5 lbs? Shade the curve to support your answer.

Algebra 1

A group of 8 female swimmers is comparing their fastest 50 meter freestyle times. These times are given in the table.

Tabitha	35.053 sec
Reece	38.230 sec
Michelle	37.529 sec
Kourtney	35.640 sec
Alexis	31.380 sec
Donna	36.950 sec
Jennifer	33.559 sec
Tamisha	30.909 sec

What are the mean and standard deviation for this group of swimmers?

How many swimmers are within one standard deviation of the mean?

Exactly how many standard deviations slower than the mean is Michelle?

Pre-Calculus

Jennifer's class was asked to randomly select 100 x-values on the interval from $-2\pi \leq x \leq 2\pi$ and generate the corresponding y-values for a sinusoidal function, g(x). Using her graphing calculator, Jennifer created a boxplot based on the class data:

g(x)

Function Values

Which of the following functions could the class have used to generate data resulting in this boxplot?

A. $g(x) = \cos(4x) - 2$ B. $g(x) = 2\cos(x) - 4$

C. $g(x) = 2\cos(x - 4)$ D. $g(x) = 4\cos(x) - 2$

E. $g(x) = 4\cos(x - 2)$

Measures of Central Tendency and Variability

ABOUT THIS LESSON

The lesson provides students with an opportunity to work with mean, median, mode, range, and mean absolute deviation, in the context of a real-world situation. The focus of the activity is for students to explore how the minimum and maximum values affect the relationship between the mean and median and how to use the mean absolute deviation as a measure of variability.

OBJECTIVES

Students will

- calculate mean, median, mode, and range.
- discover how the mean and median react to extreme values in data.
- predict the effect of changes in the data on the measures of center.
- select data to meet specific requirements for the measures of center.
- determine the mean absolute deviation.
- interpret the mean absolute deviation in context.

LEVEL

Grade 6 in a unit on statistics

MODULE/CONNECTION TO AP*

Graphical Displays and Distributions

Advanced Placement and AP are registered trademarks of the College Entrance Examination Board. The College Board was not involved in the production of this product.

MODALITY

NMSI emphasizes using multiple representations to connect various approaches to a situation in order to increase student understanding. The lesson provides multiple strategies and models for using those representations indicated by the darkened points of the star to introduce, explore, and reinforce mathematical concepts and to enhance conceptual understanding.

P – Physical
V – Verbal
A – Analytical
N – Numerical
G – Graphical

TEACHER PAGES

COMMON CORE STATE STANDARDS FOR MATHEMATICAL CONTENT

This lesson addresses the following Common Core State Standards for Mathematical Content. The lesson requires that students recall and apply each of these standards rather than providing the initial introduction to the specific skill.

Targeted Standards

6.SP.5c: Summarize numerical data sets in relation to their context, such as by:
(c) giving quantitative measures of center (median and/or mean) and variability (interquartile range and/or mean absolute deviation), as well as describing any overall pattern and any striking deviations from the overall pattern with reference to the context in which the data was gathered.
See questions 1, 2a-d, 3, 4i-o, 5-6

6.SP.5d: Summarize numerical data sets in relation to their context, such as by:
(d) relating the choice of measures of center and variability to the shape of the data distribution and the context in which the data was gathered.
See questions 2e-f, 3, 5-6

Reinforced/Applied Standards

6.SP.4: Display numerical data in plots on a number line, including dot plots, histograms, and box plots.
See question 4b

6.NS.7c: Understand ordering and absolute value of rational numbers.
(c) Understand the absolute value of a rational number as its distance from 0 on the number line, interpret absolute value as magnitude for a positive or negative quantity in a real world situation.
For example, for an account balance of –30 dollars, write |–30| = 30 to describe the size of the debt in dollars.
See questions 4e, 4g-h, 4j, 4m, 5d, 5f

T E A C H E R   P A G E S

COMMON CORE STATE STANDARDS FOR MATHEMATICAL PRACTICE

These standards describe a variety of instructional practices based on processes and proficiencies that are critical for mathematics instruction. NMSI incorporates these important processes and proficiencies to help students develop knowledge and understanding and to assist them in making important connections across grade levels. This lesson allows teachers to address the following Common Core State Standards for Mathematical Practice.

MP.2: Reason abstractly and quantitatively.
In question 3, students predict changes in the mean and median age based on changes to the values in each scenario first by considering the size of the numbers then confirming the prediction numerically. For example, students may recognize without doing any calculations that replacing Father with Grandpa James will cause the mean to increase and then confirm their prediction numerically.

MP.3: Construct viable arguments and critique the reasoning of others.
Students encounter multiple questions requiring them to justify their choice of a particular measure of center or explain their process for creating a new data set to satisfy specific criteria.

MP.8: Look for and express regularity in repeated reasoning.
After manipulating values within a data set in a variety of scenarios, students recognize the impact of extreme values on measures of center and apply their knowledge to a new situation.

FOUNDATIONAL SKILLS

The following skills lay the foundation for concepts included in this lesson:
- Calculate mean, median, mode, and range
- Create dotplots (line plots)

ASSESSMENTS

The following formative assessment is embedded in this lesson:
- Students engage in independent practice.

The following additional assessments are located on our website:
- Graphical Displays and Distributions – 6th Grade Free Response Questions
- Graphical Displays and Distributions – 6th Grade Multiple Choice Questions

MATERIALS AND RESOURCES

- Student Activity pages

TEACHER PAGES

TEACHER PAGES

TEACHING SUGGESTIONS

Before beginning the activity, review the definitions of mean, median, mode, and range. Discuss with students that the mean and median are measures of central tendency and that range represents the variability, or spread, of the data.

In question 2, the terms "nonresistant" and "resistant" measures of central tendency are introduced. A nonresistant statistic is one that is noticeably affected by extreme values in the data. The mean is a nonresistant measure of central tendency. In contrast, the median will not be affected by changes to the largest and smallest values in the data, and hence is called a resistant statistic.

As an activity to engage students in the discovery of how extreme values do and do not affect the measures of center, the teacher can make a set of paper signs for question 3 displaying each family member's name and age, along with signs for "median" and "mean". Students can then act out the various scenarios, placing the "median" and "mean" signs appropriately for a visual demonstration of the concept. As students begin to gain understanding, ask them to predict how the location of the mean and median signs should be adjusted before actually doing the calculations.

This lesson can be used to introduce mean absolute deviation or to reinforce the concept. Using the lipstick data, question 4 provides scaffolding to help students develop a process for calculating mean absolute deviation. By plotting data in a dotplot, drawing the mean and MAD boundaries, and counting the number of values within one MAD of the mean and more than one MAD from the mean, students develop a feeling for the spread of the data and how mean absolute deviation describes the overall variation of the data set. This lays a foundation for being able to look at a measure of variability and use it to describe how shape and variation in a data set are related.

Questions 1-4 are intended as a cooperative learning exercise. If this lesson is used to introduce MAD, question 4 should be a whole group activity. Questions 5 and 6 provide the opportunity for students to continue in groups or to work independently.

You may wish to support this activity with TI-Nspire™ technology. See *Finding the Mean and Median of a Data Set* in the NMSI TI-Nspire Skill Builders.

Suggested modifications for additional scaffolding include the following:

1e Provide a dotplot of the data to explain why the mean is larger than the median.

3 Provide a scaled "number line" as the students act out the scenarios. Students who are not holding the signs can predict where the mean and median should be located and then direct "mean" and "median" where to stand. Students should justify their predictions for the placements.

3a Instruct the student to list the family members and ages for each scenario before calculating the mean and median.

4b Provide a scaled number line for the dotplot.

4e Add a process column to the chart as shown in part (a).

4k Work together with the student to answer the first question by filling in blanks such as: mean _____ + MAD _____ = _____ and asking the student to help locate the numbers that fill in the blanks from the previous questions. Then instruct the student to follow the same process to answer the second question.

4n Direct the student to use the dotplot in part (b) to answer this question by marking the MAD on the dotplot.

4o Remove the two most expensive lipsticks or provide the revised mean and a table to use to calculate the new MAD value.

5f, 6f Provide a table or create a dotplot for the student to use.

NSMI CONTENT PROGRESSION CHART

In the spirit of NMSI's goal to connect mathematics across grade levels, a Content Progression Chart for each module demonstrates how specific skills build and develop from sixth grade through pre-calculus in an accelerated program that enables students to take college-level courses in high school, using a faster pace to compress content. In this sequence, Grades 6, 7, 8, and Algebra 1 are compacted into three courses. Grade 6 includes all of the Grade 6 content and some of the content from Grade 7, Grade 7 contains the remainder of the Grade 7 content and some of the content from Grade 8, and Algebra 1 includes the remainder of the content from Grade 8 and all of the Algebra 1 content.

The complete Content Progression Chart for this module is provided on our website and at the beginning of the training manual. This portion of the chart illustrates how the skills included in this particular lesson develop as students advance through this accelerated course sequence.

6th Grade Skills/Objectives	7th Grade Skills/Objectives	Algebra 1 Skills/Objectives	Geometry Skills/Objectives	Algebra 2 Skills/Objectives	Pre-Calculus Skills/Objectives
Calculate the mean, median, mode, range, and mean absolute deviation from tabular or graphical data or data presented in paragraph form.	Calculate the mean, median, mode, range, and mean absolute deviation from tabular or graphical data or data presented in paragraph form	Calculate the mean, median, mode, range, and standard deviation from tabular or graphical data or data presented in paragraph form.	Calculate the mean, median, mode, range, and standard deviation from tabular or graphical data or data presented in paragraph form.	Calculate the mean, median, mode, range, and standard deviation from tabular or graphical data or data presented in paragraph form	Calculate the mean, median, mode, range, and standard deviation from tabular or graphical data or data presented in paragraph form
Determine the effect on the mean, median, mode, range, and mean absolute deviation of making a change in the data and determine changes that do not affect the mean and/or median.	Determine the effect on the mean, median, mode, range, and mean absolute deviation of making a change in the data and determine changes that do not affect the mean and/or median.	Determine the effect on the mean, median, mode, range, and standard deviation of making a change in the data and determine changes that do not affect the mean and/or median.	Determine the effect on the mean, median, mode, range, and standard deviation of making a change in the data and determine changes that do not affect the mean and/or median.	Determine the effect on the mean, median, mode, range, and standard deviation of making a change in the data and determine changes that do not affect the mean and/or median.	Determine the effect on the mean, median, mode, range, and standard deviation of making a change in the data and determine changes that do not affect the mean and/or median.

TEACHER PAGES

TEACHER PAGES

NATIONAL
MATH + SCIENCE
INITIATIVE

Mathematics

Measures of Central Tendency and Variability

1. Samantha wants to buy a lipstick for her mother as a surprise thank you gift for driving her to practices and games during soccer season. She searches an internet site for the prices of the lipsticks that she thinks her mom might like. She creates the following price list.

Price	Price
$8.99	$9.99
$6.50	$3.39
$18.50	$7.99
$8.99	$5.99
$7.99	$3.99
$7.99	$4.99
$16.50	

Samantha is uncertain about how much money to spend. Her older brother, Rasheed, suggests that she determine the **median** price for the lipsticks and buy the brand that corresponds to that price.

a. What other word or words could be used to describe the median?

b. Describe a method of determining the median.

c. Write the prices of the lipsticks in the boxes from least to greatest. Fold the strip in half. What is the "middle" number based on the location of the crease?

d. Why is ordering the numbers an important step in locating the median?

Copyright © 2013 National Math + Science Initiative, Dallas, Texas. All rights reserved. Visit us online at www.nms.org.

11

2. Samantha is happy with her decision to buy one of the median priced lipsticks. She approaches her father to ask for his advice in buying the lipstick. He looks at the list of different lipsticks and at Samantha's choice and asks how she made her decision. Samantha explains that she determined the median price and selected one of those lipsticks as her choice. Her father asks if she knows the mean price, the mode price, or the range of prices. Samantha quickly begins to determine these values.

a. What other word is often used to describe the mean?

b. Calculate the arithmetic mean for the prices of the lipstick. Do the numbers need to be listed in order when determining the arithmetic mean? Explain.

c. Determine the mode. Should the prices of the lipstick be listed in order when determining the mode? Explain.

d. The range is a measure of variability, or spread, of the data. What is the range of the data? Explain what this value indicates in the context of the situation.

e. Why is the arithmetic mean larger than the median from question 1 for the prices of lipsticks?

f. If Samantha has to choose between the mean or median price for lipstick, which do you feel is a more appropriate representation of the center of the data? Justify your answer.

3. Samantha decides to buy the brand of lipstick she originally chose when she used the median as a method of selection, but is confused about why the median and mean prices are different. She decides to seek out her older sister, Linda, to help her understand the difference.

Since relatives often stay with the family for short periods of time, Linda decides to use the ages of the family members staying in the house at various times to help her sister understand why the values of the mean and the median may be so different.

The following scenarios are given in chronological order and provide information about the family members who are present. Each additional part of the question is based on the information from all the previous parts. For each of the scenarios, complete the following:

   i. List the family members currently living in the house.

   ii. Predict how the median age and the mean age for those family members change from the previous scenario.

   iii. Confirm your prediction by calculating the actual median age and mean age for the family members currently living in the house.

   iv. Explain why the mean and/or the median changes or stays the same.

Scenario 1:
Samantha's family consists of Rasheed (14), Mother (42), Father (44), Linda (17) and Samantha herself (11).

Scenario 2:
Father leaves to go on a month-long trip and Grandpa James, who is 68 years old, moves in to help take care of the family for that month.

Scenario 3:
Father returns home. Grandpa James leaves. Mom's sister Liz takes Samantha away to camp, but leaves her one-year old daughter, Elisa.

Scenario 4:
Samantha comes home from camp and Elisa leaves. Linda graduates from high school and leaves for college. Their younger cousin Kevin, who is 8 years old, moves in.

Scenario 5:
Great-Grandpa Charlie, who is 94 years old, needs to live with family, so he comes to live at Samantha's house. Mom goes away on a business trip.

Scenario 6:
Twin cousins Amanda and Keesha, who are 12, need a place to live. Mom comes home from her trip. Kevin and Great-Grandpa Charlie decide there are too many girls, so they leave.

a. Create a different scenario in which Linda is the median age and the mean age changes. Will the mean increase or decrease in your scenario? Explain.

b. When a measure of center is affected by changes to the extreme values in the data, (the minimum and maximum values), it is called a nonresistant measure of center. A resistant measure of center is not affected by changes to the largest and smallest values in the data. Based on your answers to the scenarios, which measure of center is resistant? Explain your reasoning.

4. Grandpa James suggests that Samantha buy one of the lipsticks that is more than one mean absolute deviation from the mean. He offers to pay for the one Samantha selects based on this measure of variability. Since Samantha does not know how to determine which lipsticks would be included, she begins to research how to calculate the mean absolute deviation.

She discovers that besides using range, which describes the difference between the minimum and maximum lipstick price, the mean absolute deviation, or MAD, can be used to describe how far the data typically varies from the mean. Deviation is the difference between the price of the lipstick and the arithmetic mean price of all the lipsticks.

a. Complete the table by subtracting the mean price of the lipstick from question 2b from each of the lipstick prices to determine the deviation.

Price	Price – Mean	Deviation
$8.99	$8.99 - $8.60	$0.39
$6.50	$6.50 - $8.60	-$2.10
$18.50		
$8.99		
$7.99		
$7.99		
$16.50		
$9.99		
$3.39		
$7.99		
$5.99		
$3.99		
$4.99		

b. Create a dotplot to show the distribution of the lipstick prices. Draw a vertical line to represent the location of the mean.

c. If the deviation between the price and the mean is positive, what does this represent in the context of the situation? What does it indicate when the deviation is negative?

d. What percent of the data is greater than the mean? What percent of the data is less than the mean?

e. Complete the table by determining the absolute value of the deviations from part (a).

Price	|Deviations|
$8.99	|$0.39|=$0.39
$6.50	|-$2.10|=$2.10
$18.50	
$8.99	
$7.99	
$7.99	
$16.50	
$9.99	
$3.39	
$7.99	
$5.99	
$3.99	
$4.99	

f. What is the sum of the absolute value of the deviations in the table?

g. The sum of the deviations in part (a) is zero. Why is the answer in part (f) not zero?

h. What does the absolute value of the deviation determined for the $18.50 tube of lipstick represent in the context of the situation?

i. The mean absolute deviation, MAD, measures variability of a data point using the distance a point is from the mean. To calculate this value, use the formula

$$MAD = \frac{sum \left| price\ of\ lipstick - mean\ price\ of\ lipstick \right|}{number\ of\ lipsticks}$$

What is the mean absolute deviation for all of the lipsticks?

j. What does the mean absolute deviation indicate in the context of the situation?

k. When a data point lies within one MAD of the mean, the price of the lipstick is less than or equal to the sum of the mean and the MAD. What is the sum of the mean and the MAD? When a data point lies within one MAD, the price of the lipstick is also greater than or equal to the MAD subtracted from the mean. What is the MAD subtracted from the mean?

l. Complete the inequality statement with your answers from part (k).
When the price of the lipstick is within one MAD of the mean, the inequality,
_____ ≤ Price of Lipstick ≤ _____ , represents these prices.

m. On the dotplot in part (b), draw vertical lines to show the boundaries of the mean plus or minus one MAD. How many lipstick prices are between these two lines? What percent of the lipstick prices is one MAD from the mean?

n. Since Grandpa James has offered to pay for one of the lipsticks that is more than one MAD from the mean, which one(s) can Samantha select? Explain.

o. If Samantha decided to eliminate the two most expensive lipsticks from the original list that she was considering, do you think the mean absolute deviation would be larger or smaller than the answer in part (i)? Explain your reasoning.

5. The following is a list of the heights of seven players on the LA Lakers 2012 basketball team.

Name:	Height (inches)
Devin Ebanks	81
Earl Clark	82
Robert Sacre	84
Steve Blake	75
Chris Duhon	73
Steve Nash	75
Dwight Howard	83

Source: www.nba.com/lakers/roster/2012

a. Leaving the data in inches as shown in the table, compute the mean and median height. What is the range of the heights of the seven players?

b. If Kobe Bryant, who is 6 feet 6 inches, replaced Steve Blake on the list, what effect, if any, would this change have on the values of the mean, the median, and the range of the data?

c. Based on your answers, _____ is a resistant measure of center and _____ is a non-resistant measure of center.

d. Complete the table, and then answer the questions that follow.

Name:	Height (inches)	|Height – mean height|
Devin Ebanks	81	$\|81 - 79\| = 2$
Earl Clark	82	
Robert Sacre	84	
Steve Blake	75	
Chris Duhon	73	
Steve Nash	75	
Dwight Howard	83	

Source: www.nba.com/lakers/roster/2012

What is the sum of the absolute deviations based on the original table? What is the mean absolute deviation for the original data?

e. What percent of the players are within one MAD of the mean? Support your answer with mathematical reasoning.

f. Robert Sacre is between one and two mean absolute deviations from the mean. To calculate the exact measure of variability, use the formula $\dfrac{|\text{Height} - \text{mean height}|}{\text{MAD}}$. How many mean absolute deviations away from the mean is Robert Sacre?

g. Are any of the players more than two mean absolute deviations from the mean? Explain your reasoning.

6. The average price of a new guitar from 1992 to 2000 is listed in the table:

Year	1992	1993	1994	1995	1996	1997	1998	1999	2000
Price	$560	$569	$579	$652	$645	$629	$583	$594	$571

Source: http://www.musictrades.com/census.html

a. Glancing at the data quickly, do you think the mean or the median will be larger? Why?

b. Compute the mean, median, and range.

c. Choose five different guitar prices from the list above so that the prices will have the largest range possible. Explain how you made your choices.

d. Compute the mean guitar price for the years 1997 to 2000. What would the average price in 2001 need to be for $590 to be the mean price for the five years 1997-2001? Explain the technique used to calculate the price in 2001.

e. From the chart provided, create two lists of five different guitar prices. The lists should have the same median but different means.

f. What is the mean absolute deviation for the guitar prices? Show the work that leads to your answer.

g. What percent of the guitar prices are within two mean absolute deviations of the mean? Explain your reasoning.

**Age of Presidents of the United States
When First Inaugurated**

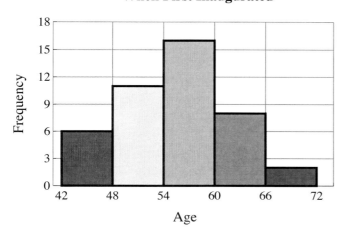

Histograms

ABOUT THIS LESSON

In this lesson, students create and interpret histograms, describe the shapes of distributions, and use the shape to predict the relationship between the mean and median. As supporting information, the lesson begins with the definitions of the two types of data and examples of each to help students determine whether a bar graph or a histogram is the appropriate choice for displaying the data.

LEVEL

Grade 6 in a unit on graphical displays

MODULE/ CONNECTION TO AP*

Graphical Displays and Distributions

Advanced Placement and AP are registered trademarks of the College Entrance Examination Board. The College Board was not involved in the production of this product.

MODALITY

NMSI emphasizes using multiple representations to connect various approaches to a situation in order to increase student understanding. The lesson provides multiple strategies and models for using those representations indicated by the darkened points of the star to introduce, explore, and reinforce mathematical concepts and to enhance conceptual understanding.

OBJECTIVES

Students will

- classify data as categorical or quantitative.
- create and interpret histograms based on quantitative data.
- describe the shape of a histogram and predict the relationship between the mean and the median based on the shape of the distribution.

TEACHER PAGES

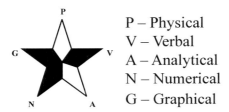

P – Physical
V – Verbal
A – Analytical
N – Numerical
G – Graphical

COMMON CORE STATE STANDARDS FOR MATHEMATICAL CONTENT

This lesson addresses the following Common Core State Standards for Mathematical Content. The lesson requires that students recall and apply each of these standards rather than providing the initial introduction to the specific skill.

Targeted Standards

6.SP.4   Display numerical data in plots on a number line, including dot plots, histograms, and box plots.
See questions 2c, 3a, 5d

6.SP.2   Understand that a set of data collected to answer a statistical question has a distribution which can be described by its center, spread, and overall shape.
See questions 3b, 3d, 5h, 5i

6.SP.5c   Summarize numerical data sets in relation to their context, such as by
(c) giving quantitative measures of center (median and/or mean) and variability (interquartile range and/or mean absolute deviation), as well as describing any overall pattern and any striking deviations from the overall pattern with reference to the context in which the data was gathered.
See questions 2a, 2e, 3c, 4b-c, 5b, 5g-i

Reinforced/Applied Standards

6.SP.5a   Summarize numerical data sets in relation to their context, such as by
(a) reporting the number of observations.
See questions 2b, 2d, 5d-f

6.SP.5d   Summarize numerical data sets in relation to their context, such as
(d) relating the choice of measures of center and variability to the shape of the data distribution and the context in which the data were gathered.
See questions 3c, 4b, 5h

6.EE.8   Write an inequality of the form $x > c$ or $x < c$ to represent a constraint or condition in a real-world or mathematical problem. Recognize that inequalities of the form $x > c$ c or $x < c$ have infinitely many solutions; represent solutions of such inequalities on number line diagrams.
See questions 2b, 5d

COMMON CORE STATE STANDARDS FOR MATHEMATICAL PRACTICE

These standards describe a variety of instructional practices based on processes and proficiencies that are critical for mathematics instruction. NMSI incorporates these important processes and proficiencies to help students develop knowledge and understanding and to assist them in making important connections across grade levels. This lesson allows teachers to address the following Common Core State Standards for Mathematical Practice.

MP.2: Reason abstractly and quantitatively.
Based solely on the overall shape of the histogram, students predict whether the mean or median is larger and then justify the prediction mathematically.

MP.5: Use appropriate tools strategically.
Students use the calculator to create histograms so that the focus is on the interpretation of the information.

MP.6: Attend to precision.
Students use inequalities to appropriately define bin widths and apply the meaning of the bin widths in interpreting the context of the problem situation.

MP.7: Look for and make use of structure.
Students relate the process of calculating the median of numerically ordered data points by counting inward from the endpoints to counting the frequencies from the end bins towards the center to determine in which bin the median is located for a histogram.

FOUNDATIONAL SKILLS

The following skills lay the foundation for concepts included in this lesson:
- Determine the median and range of data sets
- Create frequency tables

ASSESSMENTS

The following formative assessment is embedded in this lesson:
- Students engage in independent practice.

The following additional assessments are located on our website:
- Graphical Displays and Distributions – 6th Grade Free Response Questions
- Graphical Displays and Distributions – 6th Grade Multiple Choice Questions

MATERIALS AND RESOURCES

- Student Activity pages
- Colored pencils
- Graphing calculators
- Mathematica demonstration "Relating Boxplots to Histograms" explores the relationship between boxplots and histograms and is located on the NMSI website (a free download of Mathematica Player is required).
- NMSI video clip on creating histograms on the TI-84

TEACHER PAGES

TEACHING SUGGESTIONS

TEACHER PAGES

Before beginning the activity, discuss the difference between categorical and quantitative data. Categorical variables sort individuals into unique groups based on some characteristic or attribute, such as hair color, gender, or favorite food. The values of categorical variables are usually words; for example, pizza, ice cream, or hamburgers for favorite food. Quantitative variables take on numerical values for which arithmetic makes sense. Often quantitative variables come from measuring an attribute or characteristic of an individual or individuals. Examples of this might be height or weight. Other times, quantitative variables come from counting, such as populations of counties or number of children in your family.

It is possible that categorical variables have values that are made up of numerals. The variable "zip code" sorts neighborhoods into groups and is categorical. Zip codes are not a measurement or a count, and arithmetic on zip codes would not make sense. It is also possible to change a quantitative variable into a categorical variable by grouping numbers together. For example, instead of treating age as a quantitative variable, you could create age categories like 0-5 representing young children, 6-18 representing school age children, 19-25 representing young adults, and so on, and then count the number of individuals in each category.

A bar graph is used for categorical data, and a histogram is used for quantitative data. Traditionally the bars in a bar graph have spaces between them and words are provided at the base to identify each. The bars of histograms have their bases on a numerical scale that is constructed like a portion of a number line. Unless there are gaps in the data, the bars in a histogram will not have spaces between them.

The first histogram activity is based on the ages of presidents when they were first inaugurated. In this question, age is quantitative and the frequency is created using "classes" instead of categories. A class is based on continuous data and can be written as a compound inequality. (The ages of presidents in the first class are at least 42 but less than 48 years old, $42 \leq$ age of the president at inauguration < 48 .) For the salary data in the histogram activity for NFL teams, classes are also used for the frequency table. Since the data is continuous, students need to use inequality statements in the "Salary" column.

The shape of the distribution of a histogram depends on the width of each "bin" or interval. To determine the width of the bars (bin width), calculate the range of the data. One suggestion is to divide the range by five and round to the nearest whole number. The position for the first bar may be the smallest data value or a "nice" number less than the minimum. In introductory statistical analyses, histograms should be constructed so that each bar is the same width. Even if the maximum data point is not the last value in the bin, the final interval should be equal to the other bars. Changing the width of each interval changes the appearance of the graph. As a teacher-guided activity, enter the data in a list of a graphing calculator and create histograms using various x-scale settings, which determine the bin width, to see how changing the bin width changes the shape of the graph.

Depending on the objective of the lesson, the graphing calculator can be used by either the students and/or teacher to create the histograms for question 3 where the focus of the lesson pertains to the shape of the distribution and the relationship between mean and median. The use of this technology allows students to focus on how the median and mean respond to extreme values.

You may wish to support this activity with TI-Nspire™ technology. See Graphical Representations of Data in the NMSI TI-Nspire Skill Builders.

Describing the shape of a distribution and the relationship between the mean and median connects the idea of resistant and non-resistant measures of center with extreme values, (minimum and maximum data points). Use these sample histograms along with the descriptions to help students with this important concept. When describing a shape that is "skewed right" or "skewed left," students often confuse the direction. To help them, discuss that the direction of the "long tail" of the data determines the direction of the skewness.

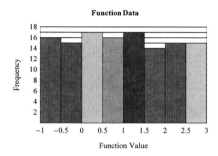

The histogram above would be described as uniform since the bins have the same or similar frequencies throughout the distribution. Since this distribution is fairly symmetric, we expect the mean and median function values to be approximately the same.

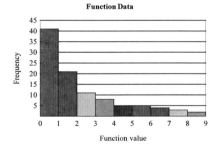

The histogram above would be described as skewed right or skewed to the larger numbers since the tail of the distribution is on the right hand side. Since this distribution is skewed right, the mean function value will typically be larger than the median.

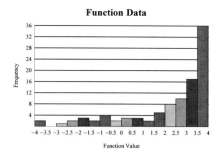

The histogram above would be described as skewed left or skewed to the smaller numbers since the tail of the distribution is on the left hand side. Since this distribution is skewed left, the mean function value will typically be less than the median.

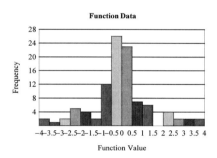

The histogram above would be described as mound shaped. Since the distribution is approximately symmetric, we expect the mean and median function values to be approximately the same.

T E A C H E R   P A G E S

Suggested modifications for additional scaffolding include the following:

2b Modify the question to complete the tally column in advance.

3 Provide the illustrations and descriptions of the four possible shapes from the Teaching Suggestions.

3a Modify the question to complete the first two rows of the table and the first two bins of the histogram.

5c Supply the bin width and starting value for the histogram.

5d Provide the completed frequency table and mark the given grid with bin widths and labels.

5i List specific topics to discuss in the paragraph.

NMSI CONTENT PROGRESSION CHART

In the spirit of NMSI's goal to connect mathematics across grade levels, a Content Progression Chart for each module demonstrates how specific skills build and develop from sixth grade through pre-calculus in an accelerated program that enables students to take college-level courses in high school, using a faster pace to compress content. In this sequence, Grades 6, 7, 8, and Algebra 1 are compacted into three courses. Grade 6 includes all of the Grade 6 content and some of the content from Grade 7, Grade 7 contains the remainder of the Grade 7 content and some of the content from Grade 8, and Algebra 1 includes the remainder of the content from Grade 8 and all of the Algebra 1 content.

The complete Content Progression Chart for this module is provided on our website and at the beginning of the training manual. This portion of the chart illustrates how the skills included in this particular lesson develop as students advance through this accelerated course sequence.

6th Grade Skills/Objectives	7th Grade Skills/Objectives	Algebra 1 Skills/Objectives	Geometry Skills/Objectives	Algebra 2 Skills/Objectives	Pre-Calculus Skills/Objectives
Create, interpret, and compare dotplots (line plots), stemplots, and bar graphs.	Create, interpret, and compare dotplots (line plots), stemplots, bar graphs, histograms, and boxplots.	Create, interpret, and compare dotplots (line plots), stemplots, bar graphs, histograms, and boxplots.	Create, interpret, and compare dotplots (line plots), stemplots, bar graphs, histograms, and boxplots.	Create, interpret, and compare dotplots (line plots), stemplots, bar graphs, histograms, and boxplots.	Create, interpret, and compare dotplots (line plots), stemplots, bar graphs, histograms, and boxplots.
Calculate the mean, median, mode, range, and mean absolute deviation from tabular or graphical data or data presented in paragraph form.	Calculate the mean, median, mode, range, and mean absolute deviation from tabular or graphical data or data presented in paragraph form	Calculate the mean, median, mode, range, and standard deviation from tabular or graphical data or data presented in paragraph form.	Calculate the mean, median, mode, range, and standard deviation from tabular or graphical data or data presented in paragraph form.	Calculate the mean, median, mode, range, and standard deviation from tabular or graphical data or data presented in paragraph form	Calculate the mean, median, mode, range, and standard deviation from tabular or graphical data or data presented in paragraph form

TEACHER PAGES

Histograms

Categorical data consists of observations that can be separated into specific categories. Some examples would be types of automobiles, states of birth, and favorite sports. Categorical data is displayed on a bar graph.

Quantitative data consists of observations with numerical values. Often quantitative data results from measurements and includes units. Some examples would be the price of a gallon of gasoline, the heights of buildings in a city, the ages of your classmates in months, and the sum resulting from the roll of two dice. Quantitative data is displayed in a histogram.

1. Based on these definitions, identify each of the following as either categorical or quantitative. Would a bar graph or histogram be an appropriate graphical display for the data?

   a. Favorite pet

   b. Number of text messages

   c. Height in inches

   d. Birth month

   e. Area code

2. The following table lists the names of 43 presidents and their ages when first inaugurated. Since age is a quantitative variable, a histogram is appropriate to display the distribution of the data. A histogram uses bars, called bins, like a bar graph; however, the horizontal axis is a portion of a number line and the bars touch unless gaps occur in the data.

Barack Obama was inaugurated as the 44th president of the United States when he was 47, one of the youngest presidents in American history. Obama is the 44th president but only 43 presidents are listed based on their age when <u>first</u> inaugurated. Cleveland served two non-consecutive terms and is listed for the first term only.

President	Age	President	Age	President	Age
Washington	57	Lincoln	52	F. D. Roosevelt	51
J. Adams	61	A. Johnson	56	Truman	60
Jefferson	57	Grant	46	Eisenhower	61
Madison	57	Hayes	54	Kennedy	43
Monroe	58	Garfield	49	L. B. Johnson	55
J. Q. Adams	57	Arthur	51	Nixon	56
Jackson	61	Cleveland	47	Ford	61
Van Buren	54	Harrison	55	Carter	52
W. H. Harrison	68	McKinley	54	Reagan	69
Tyler	51	T. Roosevelt	42	G. Bush	64
Polk	49	Taft	51	Clinton	46
Taylor	64	Wilson	56	G. W. Bush	54
Fillmore	50	Harding	55	Obama	47
Pierce	48	Coolidge	51		
Buchanan	65	Hoover	54		

a. Identify the minimum and maximum ages and determine the range of the data.

b. Complete the frequency table provided based on the bin width and minimum value for the histogram.

Age	Tally	Frequency
$42 \leq age < 48$	⦀⦀	6
$48 \leq age < 54$		
$54 \leq age < 60$		
$60 \leq age < 66$		
$66 \leq age < 72$		

c. Complete the histogram provided.

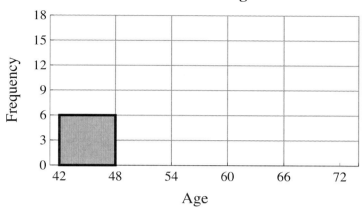

**Age of Presidents of the United States
When First Inaugurated**

d. Explain the meaning of the first bin of the graph in the context of the situation.

e. Without calculating the median, in which bin would this value be located? Explain how to determine the answer.

3. The table contains the cargo space of the 45 sports-utility vehicles available in 2002 as listed in the *Consumer Reports Auto Issue*, April 2002.

    a. Create a histogram with a bin width of 11 and a minimum value of 16.

42	35.5	45	59	40	77	59	28	39
47.5	33.5	84	45.5	39	59	77	32	33.5
34.5	39.5	43	37	35	16	30	46.5	29
50	37.5	34.5	45.5	45.5	45	33	33.5	43.5
49	37	36	37.5	44	41.5	50	36.5	59

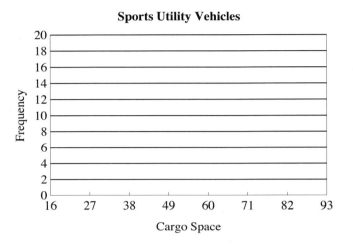

Cargo Space	Tally	Frequency
$16 \leq CS < 27$		

    b. The shape of the histogram in question 2c is "mound" shaped which means that the mean and median should be approximately the same value. Other terms that can be used to describe the shape of a distribution of a histogram are skewed left, skewed right, and uniform. What is the shape of this distribution?

    c. For this set of data, the mean is 43.211 cubic feet and the median is 40 cubic feet. Explain why the mean and median are not the same based on the shape of the distribution of the histogram.

4. The histogram shows the distribution of the length of shoes for 17 third grade students.

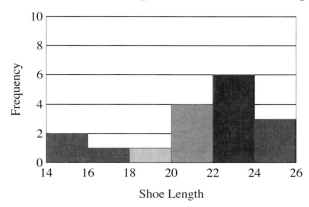

a. What is the shape of the distribution?

b. What is the expected relationship between the mean and the median? Explain the answer.

c. The exact value of the median cannot be determined from the graph. In which bin is the median located? Explain the process used to determine the answer.

5. The table displays the 2012 total salaries for each NFL team. Each salary has been "coded" by first rounding the total salary to the nearest hundred thousand and then using the nearest number of millions as the coded data value. For example, the Denver Broncos' team salary was rounded to 109,500,000 and coded as 110.

Team	Salary	Coded Data	Team	Salary	Coded Data
Arizona Cardinals	110,600,000	111	Miami Dolphins	116,600,000	117
Atlanta Falcons	117,200,000	117	Minnesota Vikings	111,700,000	112
Baltimore Ravens	115,300,000	115	New England Patriots	110,600,000	111
Buffalo Bills	112,700,000	113	New Orleans Saints	112,400,000	112
Carolina Panthers	111,400,000	111	New York Giants	117,000,000	117
Chicago Bears	114,300,000	114	New York Jets	112,500,000	113
Cincinnati Bengals	105,400,000	105	Oakland Raiders	114,600,000	115
Cleveland Browns	107,300,000	107	Philadelphia Eagles	100,400,000	100
Dallas Cowboys	105,300,000	105	Pittsburgh Steelers	116,100,000	116
Denver Broncos	109,500,000	110	Saint Louis Rams	116,600,000	117
Detroit Lions	118,300,000	118	San Diego Chargers	116,500,000	117
Green Bay Packers	109,000,000	109	San Francisco 49ers	117,200,000	117
Houston Texans	118,300,000	118	Seattle Seahawks	107,400,000	107
Indianapolis Colts	110,500,000	111	Tampa Bay Buccaneers	105,700,000	106
Jacksonville Jaguars	91,900,000	92	Tennessee Titans	103,600,000	104
Kansas City Chiefs	94,000,000	94	Washington Redskins	113,100,000	113

a. Is the data in the table categorical or quantitative? Defend your choice.

b. State the minimum and maximum values of the data and the range of the data.

c. What bin width and minimum value will be used for the frequency table and the histogram?

d. Create a frequency table and draw a histogram based on your answer in part (c). Include the inequality statements in the first columns.

Salary	Tally	Frequency

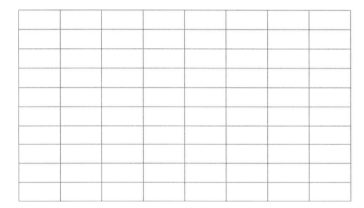

e. What is the meaning of the third bin of the graph in context of the situation?

f. In which interval are most of these NFL teams located? Interpret the answer in the context of the situation.

g. Using only the graph, in which interval is the median salary for the football players located? Justify the answer.

h. What is the shape of the graph? Based on the histogram, what is the relationship between the mean and median? Explain the answer.

i. Write a paragraph for the newspaper describing what the histogram reveals about the salaries of the NFL teams.

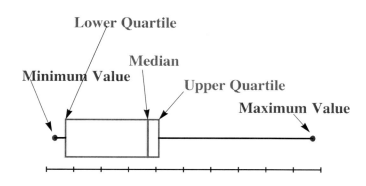

Lower Quartile

Median

Minimum Value

Upper Quartile

Maximum Value

Box-and-Whisker Plots

ABOUT THIS LESSON

In this lesson, students create and interpret box-and-whisker plots (boxplots) in context of various situations. They determine the five-number summary, and use the interquartile range, IQR, to determine whether data points are outliers. Modified boxplots, boxplots that represent outliers with points beyond the endpoints of the whisker, are used in the activity since this is the preferred method in statistics. Students construct, interpret, and compare the distributions of parallel boxplots.

LEVEL

Grade 6 or Grade 7 in a unit on graphical displays

MODULE/CONNECTION TO AP*

Graphical Displays and Distributions

Advanced Placement and AP are registered trademarks of the College Entrance Examination Board. The College Board was not involved in the production of this product.

OBJECTIVES

Students will

- determine the five-number summary for data sets.
- construct standard and modified boxplots.
- read and interpret the distribution of data represented in boxplots.
- compare data represented in parallel boxplots.

MODALITY

NMSI emphasizes using multiple representations to connect various approaches to a situation in order to increase student understanding. The lesson provides multiple strategies and models for using those representations indicated by the darkened points of the star to introduce, explore, and reinforce mathematical concepts and to enhance conceptual understanding.

P – Physical
V – Verbal
A – Analytical
N – Numerical
G – Graphical

TEACHER PAGES

TEACHER PAGES

COMMON CORE STATE STANDARDS FOR MATHEMATICAL CONTENT

This lesson addresses the following Common Core State Standards for Mathematical Content. The lesson requires that students recall and apply each of these standards rather than providing the initial introduction to the specific skill.

Targeted Standards

6.SP.4: Display numerical data in plots on a number line, including dot plots, histograms, and box plots.
See questions 1a, 2b, 3a

6.SP.5c: Summarize numerical data sets in relation to their context, such as by (c) giving quantitative measures of center (median and/or mean) and variability (interquartile range and/or mean absolute deviation), as well as describing any overall pattern and any striking deviations from the overall pattern with reference to the context in which the data was gathered.
See questions 1a, 1c-d, 1f-h, 2a-b, 3a, 3c-e

7.SP.4: Use measures of center and measures of variability for numerical data from random samples to draw informal comparative inferences about two populations. *For example, decide whether the words in a chapter of a seventh-grade science book are generally longer than the words in a chapter of a fourth-grade science book.*
See questions 2c-e, 4a-c

COMMON CORE STATE STANDARDS FOR MATHEMATICAL PRACTICE

These standards describe a variety of instructional practices based on processes and proficiencies that are critical for mathematics instruction. NMSI incorporates these important processes and proficiencies to help students develop knowledge and understanding and to assist them in making important connections across grade levels. This lesson allows teachers to address the following Common Core State Standards for Mathematical Practice.

MP.1: Make sense of problems and persevere in solving them.
Students make a human boxplot to model the effect of an extreme value on a statistical measure.

MP.2: Reason abstractly and quantitatively.
In question 3, students recognize the effect of an extreme value on the position of the mean in a data set without actually calculating the mean, and then they numerically compute the largest salary that would not be an outlier.

MP.3: Construct viable arguments and critique the reasoning of others.
In question 2e, students must use characteristics of the parallel boxplots to justify that minivans tend to have more cargo volume than SUVs.

FOUNDATIONAL SKILLS

The following skills lay the foundation for concepts included in this lesson:
- Calculate measures of central tendency
- Scale and use a number line to plot data

ASSESSMENTS

The following formative assessment is embedded in this lesson:
- Students engage in independent practice.

The following additional assessments are located on our website:
- Graphical Displays and Distributions – 6th Grade Free Response Questions
- Graphical Displays and Distributions – 6th Grade Multiple Choice Questions
- Graphical Displays and Distributions – 7th Grade Free Response Questions
- Graphical Displays and Distributions – 7th Grade Multiple Choice Questions

MATERIALS AND RESOURCES
- Student Activity pages
- Graphing calculators (optional)

TEACHER PAGES

TEACHING SUGGESTIONS

Before beginning the lesson, tell students that the purpose of a boxplot is to determine the shape of the data and easily compare and contrast two or more data sets. A technique for actively engaging students is to construct a human boxplot. Ask for 9 volunteers to arrange themselves at the front of the classroom by some physical characteristic (hair length or height are possibilities). Ask the class to identify which student is the median (5th of the 9 ordered students). Have that student turn 90°(to eliminate him/herself from the other data points), and have the student hold a sign for the median. Now there are 4 students on either side of the median. Ask the class to identify Q_1 (between the 2nd and 3rd students) and Q_3 (between the 7th and 8th students) and ask for two more volunteers to hold the signs for Q_1 and Q_3 in the space between them (indicating that Q_1 and Q_3 are not actual data points). The first and last students in the arrangements can hold signs for the minimum and maximum. In this way, students review the vocabulary and process of calculating a five-number summary while they can "see" the construction of a standard boxplot. String or yarn can be used to connect the minimum and maximum values to the "box" so that students can visualize the whiskers.

In question 1a, the boxplot is provided. Although this type of graphical display is very different from a standard coordinate graph, a consistent scale is required. Like a scatterplot or a histogram, a scale is always required on the axis below the graph. Have the students label the five-number summary on the graph before they determine the scale of the horizontal axis.

Outliers refer to any number which is at the extremes of data sets. Part (g) in question 1 asks students to determine if the minimum and maximum cargo volumes are outliers. For a boxplot, an outlier is any data point(s) that is located more than 1.5 times the length of the IQR ($Q_3 - Q_1$) from either Q_1 or Q_3. Students use the formula, $Q_1 - 1.5(IQR)$ and

$Q_3 + 1.5(IQR)$ to determine outliers. Knowledge of the existence of outliers often alerts statisticians to unusual features in the data and reminds them to examine the data more carefully.

In question 2a, students compute the five-number summary for 45 data points. Using a graphing calculator to determine these values will save time and allow students to use technology for creating the graphical display. To determine these values, enter the data in L1 using STAT, Edit. Calculate the five-number summary by pressing STAT, CALC, 1-Var Stats, ENTER. Scroll down the screen until the values are displayed. If they do not have access to a graphing calculator, provide these values for the students so they can create the boxplot. (Minimum = 16; Q_1 = 34.75; median = 40; Q_3 = 47; Maximum = 84).

Since students are asked to construct modified boxplots in question 2b, discuss how a modified boxplot differs from a standard boxplot. The boxplot in question 1a is a standard boxplot. In a standard boxplot the whiskers of the graph are drawn to the minimum and maximum data values, and the graph does not display outliers. A modified boxplot displays any outliers that are present in the data. Outliers are represented with points beyond the whiskers and the endpoints of the whiskers represent the largest and smallest values in the data that are not outliers. Both plots display the five-number summary (minimum value, lower quartile (Q_1), median, upper quartile (Q_3), and maximum value). A graphing calculator can be set to display either a standard boxplot or a modified boxplot. On the statplot menu of the TI-84, the first boxplot option is a modified boxplot and the second boxplot option is a standard boxplot.

Comparing two graphical displays is an important concept in statistics. The students create the cargo volume for the SUVs and minivans. The purpose of these questions is to help students understand that these graphical displays can be used to make decisions. Question 2e provides an opportunity to discuss this connection. In question 4, students are given parallel boxplots and asked more direct questions about the two graphs. When comparing graphs, students must use comparative language, such as "greater than, less than, or equal," and refer to both of the situations.

Determining the scale for the boxplot in question 3 may present a challenge for students. Using technology allows them to explore various scales for the data. If graphing calculators are not used, encourage students to share their graphs and how they determined the scale. As an extension to this question, ask five students to create a physical boxplot of the data in the hall. The physical representation of the outlier is very revealing.

You may wish to support this activity with TI-Nspire™ technology. See *Finding the Five Number Summary of a Data Set* and *Investigating Data Using Box Plots* in the NMSI TI-Nspire Skill Builders.

Suggested modifications for additional scaffolding include the following:

1g   Provide the method to calculate IQR and outliers, $IQR = Q_3 - Q_1$; outliers: $Q_1 - 1.5(IQR)$; $Q_3 + 1.5(IQR)$.

2a   Provide step-by-step instructions for calculating the five-number summary using a graphing calculator. If a graphing calculator is not available, provide the student with the five-number summary.

3a   Modify the question by providing the boxplot and having the student calculate the five number summary and label the data on a provided boxplot.

4b   Modify the question to ask which of the following statements is true: "The median iron composition is lower than the median magnesium composition." or "The highest iron composition and magnesium composition are about equal."

NMSI CONTENT PROGRESSION CHART

In the spirit of NMSI's goal to connect mathematics across grade levels, a Content Progression Chart for each module demonstrates how specific skills build and develop from sixth grade through pre-calculus in an accelerated program that enables students to take college-level courses in high school, using a faster pace to compress content. In this sequence, Grades 6, 7, 8, and Algebra 1 are compacted into three courses. Grade 6 includes all of the Grade 6 content and some of the content from Grade 7, Grade 7 contains the remainder of the Grade 7 content and some of the content from Grade 8, and Algebra 1 includes the remainder of the content from Grade 8 and all of the Algebra 1 content.

The complete Content Progression Chart for this module is provided on our website and at the beginning of the training manual. This portion of the chart illustrates how the skills included in this particular lesson develop as students advance through this accelerated course sequence.

6th Grade Skills/Objectives	7th Grade Skills/Objectives	Algebra 1 Skills/Objectives	Geometry Skills/Objectives	Algebra 2 Skills/Objectives	Pre-Calculus Skills/Objectives
Create, interpret, and compare dotplots (line plots), stemplots, and bar graphs.	Create, interpret, and compare dotplots (line plots), stemplots, bar graphs, histograms, and boxplots.	Create, interpret, and compare dotplots (line plots), stemplots, bar graphs, histograms, and boxplots.	Create, interpret, and compare dotplots (line plots), stemplots, bar graphs, histograms, and boxplots.	Create, interpret, and compare dotplots (line plots), stemplots, bar graphs, histograms, and boxplots.	Create, interpret, and compare dotplots (line plots), stemplots, bar graphs, histograms, and boxplots.
Calculate the mean, median, mode, range, and mean absolute deviation from tabular or graphical data or data presented in paragraph form.	Calculate the mean, median, mode, range, and mean absolute deviation from tabular or graphical data or data presented in paragraph form	Calculate the mean, median, mode, range, and standard deviation from tabular or graphical data or data presented in paragraph form.	Calculate the mean, median, mode, range, and standard deviation from tabular or graphical data or data presented in paragraph form.	Calculate the mean, median, mode, range, and standard deviation from tabular or graphical data or data presented in paragraph form.	Calculate the mean, median, mode, range, and standard deviation from tabular or graphical data or data presented in paragraph form.

TEACHER PAGES

Box-and-Whisker Plots

1. Karma's family is interested in buying a new minivan. Karma is involved with mountain bike racing, so the cargo volume is a very important consideration in buying the minivan. The table contains the cargo space of minivans available in 2002 measured in cubic feet.

Cargo Volume	Cargo Volume
98.0 cu. ft.	57.0 cu. ft.
75.5	56.5
73.5	56.5
73.5	75.5
67.0	75.5
98.0	63.0
67.0	103.5
58.5	

a. Determine the five-number summary and complete the boxplot provided, labeling the scale appropriately and indicating the value of each labeled point.

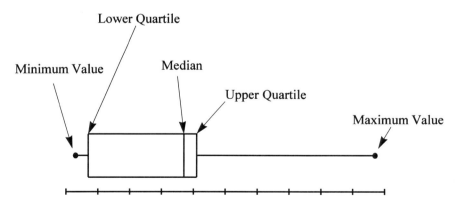

b. How does the boxplot help one visualize the data?

c. What measure(s) of central tendency can easily be identify from the boxplot? If only the boxplot is provided, what measure(s) of central tendency cannot be determined? Explain.

d. What measure(s) of spread can be easily calculated from the boxplot?

e. Sometimes data has gaps and clusters. Gaps occur when the data has large spaces between data points. Clusters occur when the data has many numbers that are very close together. Will a boxplot reveal gaps and clusters in the data? Explain.

f. Explain the significance of the data that lies between the upper and lower quartile.

g. Is the maximum or minimum value an outlier? Justify the answer by showing the process used to determine when a number is an outlier for a boxplot.

h. Suppose a vehicle with 31 cubic feet of cargo volume is classified as a minivan. Would it be considered an outlier?

2. Karma's family decides to choose one of the minivans that has the median cargo volume. Karma explains their purchase to her friend Roberto. He boasts that his family's SUV has 77 cubic feet of cargo room. Karma and Roberto argue about whether minivans or sports-utility vehicles tend to have more cargo room. Roberto searches the internet and locates data showing the cargo volumes, in cubic feet, of the 45 sports-utility vehicles available in 2002 as listed in the *Consumer Reports Auto Issue*, April 2002.

42	35.5	45	59	40	77	59	28	39
47.5	33.5	84	45.5	39	59	77	32	33.5
34.5	39.5	43	37	35	16	30	46.5	29
50	37.5	34.5	45.5	45.5	45	33	33.5	43.5
49	37	36	37.5	44	41.5	50	36.5	59

a. Using technology, calculate the five-number summary of the sports-utility vehicle data. If you do not have access to the appropriate technology, your teacher will provide the values of the 5-number summary.

b. Re-draw your boxplot from question 1 as a modified boxplot on the grid provided. Add a modified boxplot to display the SUV data.

Cargo Volume for SUVs and Minivans

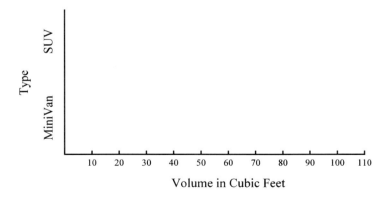

c. Do all minivans have more cargo volume than sports-utility vehicles? Explain how the graph supports the answer. Explain how one could use graphical displays of the actual data to also support the claim.

d. Can one say that the minivans that are in the upper half of the boxplot have larger cargo volume than every SUV that is not an outlier? Explain using the graphs to support the answer.

e. What are the main points that Karma should make in trying to convince Roberto that minivans tend to have more cargo volume? Be specific.

f. What advantage does the boxplot provide in comparing the SUV data that has 45 data points to the minivan data that has 15 points?

g. What information is needed to draw a back-to-back stemplot for the data? What information could be determined from the stemplot that would not be available with the boxplot? Which graphical display would you prefer for this data set? Explain your position.

3. Andrew's cousin, Samuel, is visiting from Australia. He is interested in baseball and would like to know more information about baseball players and their annual salaries. Andrew and Samuel discover the following salary information about some of their favorite players.

Baseball Player	Salary	Baseball Player	Salary
Hank Blalock	$200,000	Dave Burba	$2,000,000
Frank Catalanotto	$2,475,000	Jovanny Cedeno	$200,000
Doug Davis	$310,000	Carl Everett	$8,666,666
Juan Gonzalez	$11,000,000	Rusty Greer	$6,800,000
Bill Haselman	$800,000	Danny Kolb	$260,000
Dan Miceli	$1,000,000	Alex Rodriguez	$22,000,000

a. Create a modified boxplot for the data. Be sure to title the plot and label the five-number summary.

b. Why is it important to include a scale when displaying a boxplot? Why is it useful to label the five-number summary?

c. Why is the lower whisker so short? What does the length indicate about the data? Is it possible for a boxplot to have no lower whisker? Explain.

d. Is Alex Rodriguez an outlier? How does his salary affect the median salary? How does his salary affect the mean salary? Without actually calculating the mean salary, circle on the boxplot where the mean might be located.

e. What is the maximum salary, in whole numbers of dollars, that Alex Rodriguez could receive so that his salary would not be an outlier?

4. Twenty-six samples of Romano-British pottery were found at four different kiln sites. The percentage of oxides of two metals, magnesium and iron, measured by atomic absorption spectrophotometry, are displayed in the given boxplots.

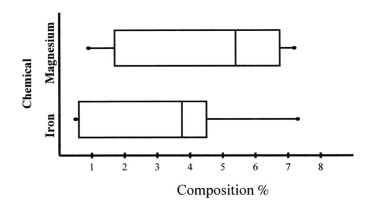

a. Approximately how much larger is the median percent of magnesium than the median percent of iron?

b. Based on the graphs, make two statements about the differences in the percent of iron and magnesium.

c. Which oxide has a larger IQR? Explain how to determine the answer.

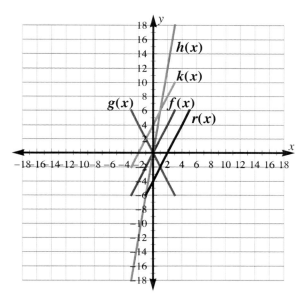

Linear Functions, Transformations, and Graphical Displays

ABOUT THIS LESSON

This lesson is designed to improve students' understanding of transformations, as well as, to provide additional practice in creating and interpreting graphical displays. Students assess the effect of transformations on function values, given a discrete domain. Through the use of the five-number summary and the boxplot, students identify how the distribution of function values changes based on different transformations of the parent function.

OBJECTIVES

Students will

- determine five-number summaries for data sets.
- graph data sets of y-values using boxplots.
- evaluate the behavior of function values when parent functions are transformed on restricted domains.
- write equations for linear functions based on the information obtained from a five-number summary.

LEVEL

Algebra 1 or Math 1 in a unit on function transformations

MODULE/CONNECTION TO AP*

Analysis of Functions
Graphical Displays and Distributions

Advanced Placement and AP are registered trademarks of the College Entrance Examination Board. The College Board was not involved in the production of this product.

MODALITY

NMSI emphasizes using multiple representations to connect various approaches to a situation in order to increase student understanding. The lesson provides multiple strategies and models for using those representations indicated by the darkened points of the star to introduce, explore, and reinforce mathematical concepts and to enhance conceptual understanding.

P – Physical
V – Verbal
A – Analytical
N – Numerical
G – Graphical

TEACHER PAGES

COMMON CORE STATE STANDARDS FOR MATHEMATICAL CONTENT

This lesson addresses the following Common Core State Standards for Mathematical Content. The lesson requires that students recall and apply each of these standards rather than providing the initial introduction to the specific skill. The star symbol (★) at the end of a specific standard indicates that the high school standard is connected to modeling.

Targeted Standards

F-BF.3: Identify the effect on the graph of replacing $f(x)$ by $f(x) + k$, $k f(x)$, $f(kx)$, and $f(x + k)$ for specific values of k (both positive and negative); find the value of k given the graphs. Experiment with cases and illustrate an explanation of the effects on the graph using technology. *Include recognizing even and odd functions from their graphs and algebraic expressions for them.*
See questions 4e, 5c-f, 6e-h, 7b-c, 8-9

S-ID.3: Interpret differences in shape, center, and spread in the context of the data sets, accounting for possible effects of extreme data points (outliers).★
See questions 4e, 5g, 6d, 7a

Reinforced/Applied Standards

S-ID.1: Represent data with plots on the real number line (dot plots, histograms, and box plots).★
See questions 1d, 2d, 3c, 4d, 5a, 6b, 7a

F-IF.2: Use function notation, evaluate functions for inputs in their domains, and interpret statements that use function notation in terms of a context.
See questions 1a, 2a, 3a, 4a

A-CED.2: Create equations in two or more variables to represent relationships between quantities; graph equations on coordinate axes with labels and scales.★
See questions 5d, 6e, 7b

COMMON CORE STATE STANDARDS FOR MATHEMATICAL PRACTICE

These standards describe a variety of instructional practices based on processes and proficiencies that are critical for mathematics instruction. NMSI incorporates these important processes and proficiencies to help students develop knowledge and understanding and to assist them in making important connections across grade levels. This lesson allows teachers to address the following Common Core State Standards for Mathematical Practice.

MP.1: Make sense of problems and persevere in solving them.
Students make connections between two seemingly unrelated topics, univariate data and linear functions, by using the five-number summary to describe the range values.

Students explain why the boxplot is translated in a different direction than the function graph.

MP.2: Reason abstractly and quantitatively.
Students use their knowledge of transformations of linear functions to predict the five-number summary for a large set of function values.

Students apply their knowledge of boxplots and transformations to write the equations of transformed functions and compare their graphs.

MP.5: Use appropriate tools strategically.
Students use a graphing calculator to generate large sets of domain values with the sequence feature, to evaluate those values in particular functions, and to predict the five-number summary for a large data set.

MP.7: Look for and make use of structure.
Students make connections between transformations of linear functions and the five-number summary of range values and apply their knowledge to answer question 6 without graphing the function or boxplot.

MP.8: Look for and express regularity in repeated reasoning.
Students observe the pattern that develops in the five-number summary of a data set as the number of data points increases and then use the pattern to predict a limiting value.

TEACHER PAGES

FOUNDATIONAL SKILLS

The following skills lay the foundation for concepts included in this lesson:

- Evaluate functions for specific domain values
- Create boxplots
- Graph linear functions with limited domains
- Compute the median and range of a set of data
- Identify equations of transformations of linear graphs

ASSESSMENTS

The following types of formative assessments are embedded in this lesson:

- Students engage in independent practice.
- Students summarize a process or procedure.

The following additional assessments are located on our website:

- Graphical Displays and Distributions – Algebra 1 Free Response Questions
- Graphical Displays and Distributions – Algebra 1 Multiple Choice Questions

MATERIALS AND RESOURCES

- Student Activity pages
- Colored pencils (optional)
- Graphing calculators
- Colored beads, 2 different colors
- Mathematica demonstration "Linear Functions and Boxplots" shows the quartiles approaching a limit and is located on the NMSI website (a free download of Mathematica Player is required).

TEACHER PAGES

TEACHING SUGGESTIONS

This lesson is designed to allow students to explore the effects of transformations on function values and how these changes are reflected in the corresponding boxplots. Before beginning this lesson, review the vocabulary associated with boxplots. The middle grades lesson, Box-and-Whisker Plots, provides clear, delineated steps on how to determine the five-number summary and create a boxplot. This activity provides another way to review and reinforce the concepts used to create a boxplot.

In this lesson, students will determine the set of y-values for a linear function with a given discrete domain and create a boxplot of the function values based on the five-number summary: the minimum value, Q_1 (the lower quartile), the median, Q_3 (the upper quartile), and the maximum value of the data. Remind students that Q_1 and Q_3 are the medians of the lower and upper half of the data.

Since the functions are continuous over a specific interval with a specific domain, it is impossible to determine the median, as well as the lower, and upper quartiles. These values will be established after the first activity.

Use question 1 to introduce the connection between function values and a boxplot of the distribution of the y-values. Each pair of students will need at least 15 beads of one color and 5 beads of another color. Instruct the students to place beads on the x-axis to represent the given domain in question 1a. As students evaluate $f(x) = 2x$ for each of the domain values, have them "plot" the ordered pairs using the beads. Have students move the beads from their coordinate points to the corresponding y-values on the y-axis and discuss the range of the function. Turn the graph paper clockwise 90 degrees and lead the students through determining the five-number summary of function values. Use a different colored bead to indicate the five-number summary on the grid. At this point, students can visualize the distribution of the y-values of the function.

Repeat the entire activity using the domain $\{-3, -2.5, -2, -1.5, -1, -0.5, 0, 0.5, 1, 1.5, 2, 2.5, 3\}$. Ask the students to determine the five-number summary and then discuss any changes they noticed.

As a follow up, discuss what they think would happen if they evaluated the function using $\frac{1}{4}$ increments. This physical representation of domain and range helps students develop a conceptual understanding between the terminology and the concept along with how transformations impact distribution of function values. Using this "bead" activity throughout this lesson will help students understand the relationship between the function values and the shape of the boxplot.

In question 2 of the activity, students will use a graphing calculator to generate function values for a discrete domain and then explore the five-number summary for the data set of y-values. As students explore the five-number summary for each set of function values, the minimum, maximum, and median values will remain the same, whereas, the values for Q_1 and Q_3 will approach -3 and 3, respectively, as the number of data points becomes extremely large. These values, which represent the y-coordinates of the midpoint of the line segment between the minimum and the median y-value and the midpoint of the line segment between the median and maximum y-value, will be used as the theoretical lower and upper quartiles in the rest of the activity.

TEACHER PAGES

In questions 3-7, students will construct boxplots based on transformations of a linear function using a given five-number summary. The purpose of this activity is to discover the effects of function transformations on the distribution of function values. The first five questions are designed to lead students through several transformations of a function and how these affect the five-number summary and shape of the boxplot. Question 8 provides students with the opportunity to apply what they have learned by predicting the five-number summary for the transformations of a different linear function over restricted domains. The final question asks the students to connect the effect of a, h, and k for the transformational form of a linear function, $y = a\,f(x-h)+k$, with the distribution of function values. This form is derived from the point-slope formula for a linear equation.

You may wish to support this activity with TI-Nspire™ technology. *See Defining a Sequence in a Spreadsheet, Finding the Five Number Summary of a Data Set,* and *Investigating Data Using Box Plots* in the NMSI TI-Nspire Skill Builders.

Suggested modifications for additional scaffolding include the following:

8   Fill in all of the values for part (a) and at least one value in each of parts (b) – (g).

9   Modify the question to say, "Summarize the effect of either a, h, or k for the transformation, $a\,f(x-h)+k$, on the distribution of function values from $f(x)$. Use your responses from the previous questions to justify your answer."

NMSI CONTENT PROGRESSION CHART

In the spirit of NMSI's goal to connect mathematics across grade levels, a Content Progression Chart for each module demonstrates how specific skills build and develop from sixth grade through pre-calculus in an accelerated program that enables students to take college-level courses in high school, using a faster pace to compress content. In this sequence, Grades 6, 7, 8, and Algebra 1 are compacted into three courses. Grade 6 includes all of the Grade 6 content and some of the content from Grade 7, Grade 7 contains the remainder of the Grade 7 content and some of the content from Grade 8, and Algebra 1 includes the remainder of the content from Grade 8 and all of the Algebra 1 content.

The complete Content Progression Chart for this module is provided on our website and at the beginning of the training manual. This portion of the chart illustrates how the skills included in this particular lesson develop as students advance through this accelerated course sequence.

6th Grade Skills/Objectives	7th Grade Skills/Objectives	Algebra 1 Skills/Objectives	Geometry Skills/Objectives	Algebra 2 Skills/Objectives	Pre-Calculus Skills/Objectives
Create, interpret, and compare dotplots (line plots), stemplots, and bar graphs.	Create, interpret, and compare dotplots (line plots), stemplots, bar graphs, histograms, and boxplots.	Create, interpret, and compare dotplots (line plots), stemplots, bar graphs, histograms, and boxplots.	Create, interpret, and compare dotplots (line plots), stemplots, bar graphs, histograms, and boxplots.	Create, interpret, and compare dotplots (line plots), stemplots, bar graphs, histograms, and boxplots.	Create, interpret, and compare dotplots (line plots), stemplots, bar graphs, histograms, and boxplots.
Calculate the mean, median, mode, range, and mean absolute deviation from tabular or graphical data or data presented in paragraph form.	Calculate the mean, median, mode, range, and mean absolute deviation from tabular or graphical data or data presented in paragraph form	Calculate the mean, median, mode, range, and standard deviation from tabular or graphical data or data presented in paragraph form.	Calculate the mean, median, mode, range, and standard deviation from tabular or graphical data or data presented in paragraph form.	Calculate the mean, median, mode, range, and standard deviation from tabular or graphical data or data presented in paragraph form	Calculate the mean, median, mode, range, and standard deviation from tabular or graphical data or data presented in paragraph form

TEACHER PAGES

55

Linear Functions, Transformations, and Graphical Displays

1. a. Let $f(x) = 2x$. On the graph paper located at the end of question 1, place beads on the x-axis to represent the domain $\{-3, -2, -1, 0, 1, 2, 3\}$. Evaluate $f(x)$ for each of the domain values by moving the beads to the corresponding ordered pair, $(x, f(x))$. List these ordered pairs.

    b. Move each bead to the corresponding y-value on the y-axis. What is the range for the function $f(x)$?

    c. Rotate the graph 90 degrees clockwise. Use a different colored bead to indicate the five-number summary on the graph. What is the five-number summary for the function values in part (a)?

    d. Explain the meaning of the five-number summary in context.

    e. Draw a boxplot based on the five-number summary from part (c).

f. Place beads on the x-axis to represent the domain $\{-3, -2.5, -2, -1.5, -1, -0.5, 0, 0.5, 1, 1.5, 2, 2.5, 3\}$. Evaluate $f(x)$ for each of the domain values by moving the beads to the corresponding ordered pair, $(x, f(x))$. What is the range for the function? Then, move each bead to the corresponding y-value on the y-axis. What is the range of the function?

g. Rotate the graph 90° clockwise. Use a different color bead to indicate the five-number summary on the graph. What is the five-number summary for the function values in part (f)? How are these values different than the values in part (c)?

h. Draw a boxplot based on the five-number summary from part (g).

i. How will the five-number summary change if the function is evaluated using the same domain as part (a) but with increments of $\frac{1}{4}$? Explain your reasoning.

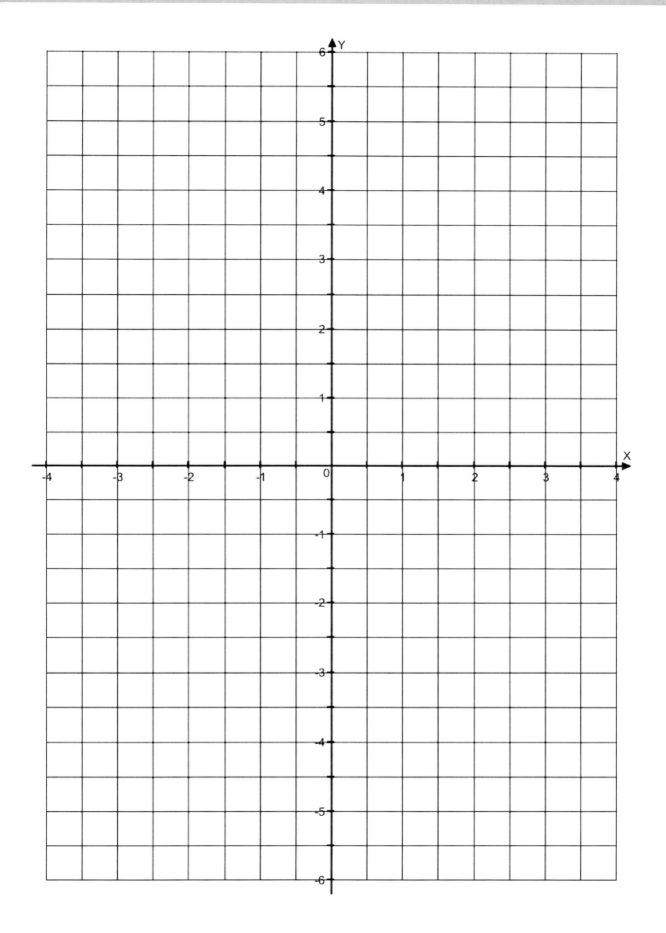

2. Evaluate the function, $f(x) = 2x$, for the following domains, using the sequence feature on the graphing calculator, and record the five-number summary for each set of function values in the table.

The key strokes for the first row of the table for increments of $\frac{1}{4}$ are as follows.

Step 1: Press [2nd] [STAT] arrow over to OPS and press seq(

Step 2: Press [X,T,Θ,n] [ENTER] [X,T,Θ,n] [ENTER] [−] [3] [ENTER] [3] [ENTER] [1] [÷] [4] [ENTER] [ENTER]

```
         seq
Expr:X
Variable:X
start: -3
end:3
step:1/4■
Paste
```

Step 3: [STO▶] [2nd] [1] [ENTER]

```
seq(X,X,-3,3,1/4
)→L₁
{-3 -2.75 -2.5 …
```

To evaluate a function for each domain value, enter the function into Y1 and then use the following steps:

Step 1: Press [STAT], press [1], arrow to the header of L2 and press [CLEAR], press [ENTER]

Step 2: Arrow to the header of L2, press [ALPHA] [TRACE] [ENTER]

Step 3: Press [(], [2nd], [1], [)] then press [ENTER]

```
L1       L2      L3      2
-3      ------  ------
-2.75
-2.5
-2.25
-2
-1.75
-1.5
L2 =Y₁(L₁)■
```

To determine the five-number summary of the function values, use these steps from the home screen:

Step 1: Press [STAT], arrow over to CALC, press [1]

Step 2: Press [2nd], [2]

Step 3: Press [ENTER], [ENTER], [ENTER]

```
      1-Var Stats
List:L₂
FreqList:
Calculate
```

The five-number summary is displayed in the second screen.

```
1-Var Stats          1-Var Stats
x̄=0                  ↑n=25
Σx=0                  minX=-6
Σx²=325               Q₁=-3.25
Sx=3.679900361        Med=0
σx=3.605551275        Q₃=3.25
↓n=25                 maxX=6
```

a.

Domain	Number of Function Values	Min	Q_1	Median	Q_3	Maximum
$x = \left\{-3, -2\frac{3}{4}, -2\frac{1}{2}, \ldots 2\frac{1}{2}, 2\frac{3}{4}, 3\right\}$						
$x = \left\{-3, -2\frac{7}{8}, -2\frac{3}{4}, \ldots 2\frac{3}{4}, 2\frac{7}{8}, 3\right\}$						
$x = \left\{-3, -2\frac{15}{16}, -2\frac{14}{16}\ldots, 2\frac{14}{16}, 2\frac{15}{16}, 3\right\}$						
$x = \left\{-3, -2\frac{31}{32}, -2\frac{30}{32}\ldots, 2\frac{30}{32}, 2\frac{31}{32}, 3\right\}$						
$x = \left\{-3, -2\frac{63}{64}, -2\frac{62}{64}\ldots, 2\frac{62}{64}, 2\frac{63}{64}, 3\right\}$						

b. Based on the table, predict the five-number summary for the function values if increments of $\frac{1}{128}$ are used to generate the domain values.

c. As the number of domain values increases, the number of function values also increases. As the number becomes extremely large, the values for Q_1 and Q_3 will approach a limiting value. Predict the integer values of the five-number summary for an extremely large set of function values.

d. Create a boxplot based on your answer in part (c).

3. Using the grid on the summary sheet provided at the end of the student activity, sketch and label $f(x) = 2x$ on the interval $-3 \leq x \leq 3$.

    a. What is the minimum y-value based on the graph? What is the maximum y-value?

    b. Write an inequality that describes the y-values for the function.

    c. Draw a boxplot on the summary sheet provided at the end of the student activity for the predicted five-number summary from question 2c.

4. The function, $g(x)$ is defined as the opposite of $f(x)$, $g(x) = -f(x)$, or a reflection of $y = 2x$ across the x-axis. Graph and label $g(x)$ on the domain, $-3 \leq x \leq 3$, using a different color pencil on the same grid as $f(x)$ on the summary sheet at the end of the student activity.

    a. Determine the minimum and maximum values of the function. Use an inequality to describe the range of the function.

    b. What is the difference between the minimum and maximum values of the function?

    c. What is the predicted median y-value?

    d. Predict the five-number summary for an extremely large set of function values, and graph the boxplot on the summary sheet provided at the end of the student activity.

    e. Compare and contrast the graphs for $f(x)$ and $g(x)$. Discuss reasons for the similarities and/or differences. Compare and contrast the boxplots for the large data sets of function values from $f(x)$ and $g(x)$. Discuss reasons for the similarities and/or differences.

5. The five-number summary for an extremely large set of function values of $h(x)$, a transformation of $f(x)$ over the same domain, $-3 \le x \le 3$, is:

    $$\text{min} = -18; Q_1 = -9; \text{median} = 0; Q_3 = 9; \text{max} = 18.$$

    a. Draw the boxplot on the summary sheet provided at the end of the student activity.

    b. Describe the range of the function using an inequality.

    c. Based on the range of $f(x)$, what scale factor was used to create the range for $h(x)$?

    d. Write the equation of $h(x)$ and sketch and label the new function using a different color pencil on the same grid as $f(x)$ on the summary sheet provided at the end of the student activity.

    e. Describe the transformation used to create $h(x)$ based on the function, $f(x)$.

    f. If $h(x)$ is reflected across the x-axis to create $w(x)$, determine the minimum and maximum values without graphing.

    g. Would the five-number summary for $w(x)$ be the same or different from $h(x)$? Explain your reasoning.

6. The five-number summary for an extremely large set of function values of $k(x)$, a transformation of $f(x)$ over the same domain, $-3 \le x \le 3$, is:

    $$\text{min} = -2; Q_1 = 1; \text{median} = 4; Q_3 = 7; \text{max} = 10.$$

    a. Describe the range of the function using an inequality.

    b. Draw the boxplot on the summary sheet provided at the end of the student activity.

    c. Based on the five-number summary for $f(x)$, how was the five-number summary for $k(x)$ determined?

d. How is the boxplot for $k(x)$ different from the boxplot for $f(x)$? How is the boxplot the same for both functions?

e. What is the equation for $k(x)$? Sketch and label the graph of $k(x)$ using a different color pencil on the same grid as $f(x)$ on the summary sheet at the end of the student activity.

f. Describe the transformation used to create $k(x)$ based on the function, $f(x)$.

g. Explain why the boxplot was translated a different direction than the coordinate graph.

h. Predict the five-number summary for $p(x) = f(x) - 2$. Explain your reasoning.

7. The five-number summary for an extremely large set of function values of $r(x)$, a transformation of $f(x)$, is:

$$\text{min} = -6; \ Q_1 = -3; \ \text{median} = 0; \ Q_3 = 3; \ \text{max} = 6.$$

a. Draw the boxplot on the summary sheet provided at the end of the student activity. How does this graphical display compare to the boxplot for $f(x)$?

b. Other than a reflection, what type of transformation could be applied to $f(x)$ that would create $r(x)$? Write an equation for $r(x)$ in point-slope form and state its domain.

c. Predict the five-number summary for $s(x) = f(x+4)$ and state the appropriate domain for this transformation.

8. For each of the following functions, predict the five-number summary for an extremely large set of function values, given that $f(x) = 3x$.

    a. $f(x)$, $0 \leq x \leq 8$

    min: _____ ; $Q1$: _____ ; med: _____ ; $Q3$: _____ ; max: _____

    b. $g(x) = -f(x)$, $0 \leq x \leq 8$

    min: _____ ; $Q1$: _____ ; med: _____ ; $Q3$: _____ ; max: _____

    c. $h(x) = 3f(x)$, $0 \leq x \leq 8$

    min: _____ ; $Q1$: _____ ; med: _____ ; $Q3$: _____ ; max: _____

    d. $k(x) = \dfrac{1}{3} f(x)$, $0 \leq x \leq 8$

    min: _____ ; $Q1$: _____ ; med: _____ ; $Q3$: _____ ; max: _____

    e. $p(x) = f(x) + 2$, $0 \leq x \leq 8$

    min: _____ ; $Q1$: _____ ; med: _____ ; $Q3$: _____ ; max: _____

    f. $s(x) = 2f(x) - 3$, $0 \leq x \leq 8$

    min: _____ ; $Q1$: _____ ; med: _____ ; $Q3$: _____ ; max: _____

    g. $r(x) = f(x - 2)$, $2 \leq x \leq 10$

    min: _____ ; $Q1$: _____ ; med: _____ ; $Q3$: _____ ; max: _____

9. Summarize the effect of *a, h,* and *k* for the transformation, $a f(x - h) + k$, on the distribution of function values from $f(x)$. Use your responses from the previous questions to justify your answers.

Summary Sheet for questions 3-7

(3c)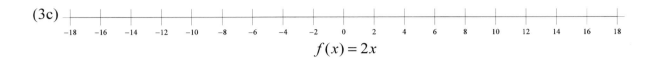

$$f(x) = 2x$$

(4d)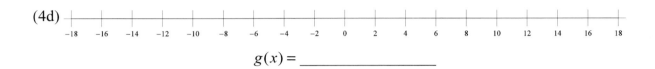

$$g(x) = \underline{\hspace{4cm}}$$

(5a)

$$h(x) = \underline{\hspace{4cm}}$$

(6b)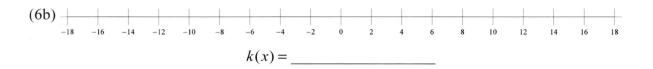

$$k(x) = \underline{\hspace{4cm}}$$

(7a)

$$r(x) = \underline{\hspace{4cm}}$$

Use this grid to graph the equations from questions 3-7.

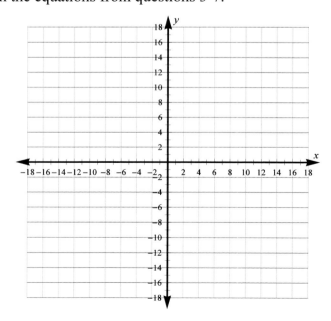

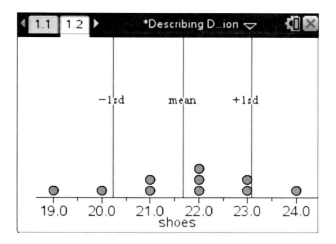

Describing Distributions: Standard Deviation

ABOUT THIS LESSON

The lesson begins with an explanation of computing standard deviation by hand. Students are given an opportunity to develop an understanding of the computation of standard deviation and then they are asked questions intended to build a conceptual understanding of standard deviation as a measurement of variability. Students should be comfortable with measures of center and have a working knowledge of shapes of distributions.

LEVEL

Algebra 1 or Math 1 in a unit on graphical displays and distributions

MODULE/CONNECTION TO AP*

Graphical Displays and Distributions

Advanced Placement and AP are registered trademarks of the College Entrance Examination Board. The College Board was not involved in the production of this product.

OBJECTIVES

Students will

- compute deviations and standard deviations by hand and with technology.
- interpret standard deviation as a measure of spread.
- describe individual data points in terms of the number of standard deviations away from the mean they fall.
- compare distributions using mean and standard deviation.
- compare individuals across distributions using mean and standard deviation.

MODALITY

NMSI emphasizes using multiple representations to connect various approaches to a situation in order to increase student understanding. The lesson provides multiple strategies and models for using those representations indicated by the darkened points of the star to introduce, explore, and reinforce mathematical concepts and to enhance conceptual understanding.

P – Physical
V – Verbal
A – Analytical
N – Numerical
G – Graphical

TEACHER PAGES

TEACHER PAGES

COMMON CORE STATE STANDARDS FOR MATHEMATICAL CONTENT

This lesson addresses the following Common Core State Standards for Mathematical Content. The lesson requires that students recall and apply each of these standards rather than providing the initial introduction to the specific skill. The star symbol (*) at the end of a specific standard indicates that the high school standard is connected to modeling.

Targeted Standards

S-ID.3: Interpret differences in shape, center, and spread in the context of the data sets, accounting for possible effects of extreme data points (outliers).*
See questions 1a-e, 2-4

S-ID.2: Use statistics appropriate to the shape of the data distribution to compare center (mean, median) and spread (interquartile range, standard deviation) of two or more different data sets.
See questions 1f, 5b-f

Reinforced/Applied Standards

S-ID.1: Represent data with plots on the real number line (dot plots, histograms, and box plots).*
See question 5a

COMMON CORE STATE STANDARDS FOR MATHEMATICAL PRACTICE

These standards describe a variety of instructional practices based on processes and proficiencies that are critical for mathematics instruction. NMSI incorporates these important processes and proficiencies to help students develop knowledge and understanding and to assist them in making important connections across grade levels. This lesson allows teachers to address the following Common Core State Standards for Mathematical Practice.

MP.1: Make sense of problems and persevere in solving them.
In question 5f, students determine the information needed to compare relative standing between the fish with largest weight gain from each group.

MP.6: Attend to precision.
Students use accurate mathematical language when describing distributions of data.

MP.7: Look for and make use of structure.
Students recognize how the standard deviation is computed and use the formula to answer a question about how an extreme value affects the standard deviation of a distribution.

FOUNDATIONAL SKILLS

The following skills lay the foundation for concepts included in this lesson:

- Create graphical displays of data using technology
- Calculate and interpret measures of central tendency

ASSESSMENTS

The following types of formative assessments are embedded in this lesson:

- Students engage in independent practice.
- Students summarize a process or procedure.

The following additional assessments are located on our website:

- Graphical Displays and Distributions – Algebra 1 Free Response Questions
- Graphical Displays and Distributions – Algebra 1 Multiple Choice Questions

MATERIALS AND RESOURCES

- Student Activity pages
- Graphing calculators

T E A C H E R   P A G E S

TEACHING SUGGESTIONS

When describing distributions, it is important to be able to summarize key characteristics of the distribution of data succinctly. Typically, values are reported for a measure of center, and of spread or variability, along with a description of the shape of the distribution. As a reminder for students, discuss that shape is described using terms such as: skewed left, skewed right, mound-shaped, and uniformly distributed. Center is most often described by either the arithmetic mean or median value.

Variability is often described using the range, however, range only gives the maximum distance between two values in the distribution. Frequently, more information is desired about the rest of the distribution. Standard deviation is the average or typical variation that a data point deviates from the mean of the distribution of data. Typically when the mean is reported for the measure of center, the standard deviation is reported as the measure of spread.

The amount a data point deviates from the mean is called its deviation from the mean. This value is determined by subtracting the mean value, μ, from the data point, x, symbolized by $x - \mu$. If a single number is desired as a description of the overall deviations from the mean, calculating the average deviation from the mean would be a natural first step; however, this process will not work, since the sum of the deviations from the mean is zero. Instead, square the deviations to combine them. The average of the squared deviations is called the variance of the distribution. Because variance has squared units, it is typically not used in combination with the mean, but rather, the positive square root of the variance, the standard deviation, is used as the description of variability in symmetric distributions

of data. Since the deviations are squared in this calculation, large deviations from the mean affect the value of the standard deviation more than small deviations from the mean which indicates that standard deviation is a non-resistant measure of variability. For this reason, standard deviation is not typically used to describe distributions that are not symmetric in shape.

Standard deviation, represented by the lowercase Greek letter "sigma," σ, is a measurement of variability within a distribution. The standard deviation of a distribution is calculated using the formula $\sigma = \sqrt{\dfrac{\sum (x_i - \mu)^2}{n}}$ where x_i is the ith value in the distribution, the Greek letter "mu," μ, is the mean of the distribution, n is the number of values in the distribution, and the capital Greek letter "sigma," Σ, indicates summing the terms. In stastistics, μ is the mean a population, whereas, $\bar{x}$ is the mean of a sample of a population. Since the calculator cannot determine whether an entire population or a sample of the population has been entered in a list, it uses $\bar{x}$ to indicate the mean of an entire population or a sample of the population.

A note of caution for question 3: the "faster" times actually refer to the athletes who ran at faster speeds and, therefore, completed the sprints in shorter times. Some students may need help in grasping this notion. Teachers should be prepared with some leading questions to help students reach this conclusion for themselves. Remember that "productive struggle" is a positive activity in any learning situation. Question 3f, by contrast, asks about "standard deviations above the mean," which does imply times that are greater in value than the mean value.

You may wish to support this activity with TI-Nspire™ technology. See *Graphical Representations of Data* in the NMSI TI-Nspire Skill Builders.

Suggested modifications for additional scaffolding include the following:

1b, c Provide answer choices to use to fill in the blanks. For example, some answer choices could be mean, median, 7, 2, etc.

1f   Provide the number of standard deviations for James and Mekia and ask the students to make the comparison.

2b   Provide the information for the first two rows of the table.

2e   Provide a fill-in-the blank statement along with answer choices. For example, "The mean decreased because the small dog is _____ _____ the minimum weight of the larger dogs." Sample answer choices could be "less than", "greater than", or "the same." For the second part of the question, provide the beginning of the response. For example, "The standard deviation increased because …"

3c   Provide a dotplot of the sprint times for this question and have the student draw in vertical lines for the mean and one standard deviation above and below the mean.

4f   Provide the beginning statement of the paragraph along with a word bank of statistical words.

5a   Provide the histogram for Group A.

TEACHER PAGES

NMSI CONTENT PROGRESSION CHART

In the spirit of NMSI's goal to connect mathematics across grade levels, a Content Progression Chart for each module demonstrates how specific skills build and develop from sixth grade through pre-calculus in an accelerated program that enables students to take college-level courses in high school, using a faster pace to compress content. In this sequence, Grades 6, 7, 8, and Algebra 1 are compacted into three courses. Grade 6 includes all of the Grade 6 content and some of the content from Grade 7, Grade 7 contains the remainder of the Grade 7 content and some of the content from Grade 8, and Algebra 1 includes the remainder of the content from Grade 8 and all of the Algebra 1 content.

The complete Content Progression Chart for this module is provided on our website and at the beginning of the training manual. This portion of the chart illustrates how the skills included in this particular lesson develop as students advance through this accelerated course sequence.

6th Grade Skills/Objectives	7th Grade Skills/Objectives	Algebra 1 Skills/Objectives	Geometry Skills/Objectives	Algebra 2 Skills/Objectives	Pre-Calculus Skills/Objectives
Create, interpret, and compare dotplots (line plots), stemplots, and bar graphs.	Create, interpret, and compare dotplots (line plots), stemplots, bar graphs, histograms, and boxplots.	Create, interpret, and compare dotplots (line plots), stemplots, bar graphs, histograms, and boxplots.	Create, interpret, and compare dotplots (line plots), stemplots, bar graphs, histograms, and boxplots.	Create, interpret, and compare dotplots (line plots), stemplots, bar graphs, histograms, and boxplots.	Create, interpret, and compare dotplots (line plots), stemplots, bar graphs, histograms, and boxplots.
Calculate the mean, median, mode, range, and mean absolute deviation from tabular or graphical data or data presented in paragraph form.	Calculate the mean, median, mode, range, and mean absolute deviation from tabular or graphical data or data presented in paragraph form	Calculate the mean, median, mode, range, and mean absolute deviation from tabular or graphical data or data presented in paragraph form.	Calculate the mean, median, mode, range, and mean absolute deviation from tabular or graphical data or data presented in paragraph form.	Calculate the mean, median, mode, range, and mean absolute deviation from tabular or graphical data or data presented in paragraph form.	Calculate the mean, median, mode, range, and mean absolute deviation from tabular or graphical data or data presented in paragraph form.

TEACHER PAGES

Describing Distributions: Standard Deviation

To summarize the variability in a data set, a value called the standard deviation can be used. The standard deviation is the typical variation that a data point varies from the mean of the distribution of data. Standard deviation of a distribution, represented by the lowercase Greek letter "sigma," σ,

is calculated using the formula $\sigma = \sqrt{\dfrac{\sum(x_i - \mu)^2}{n}}$ where x_i is the ith value in the distribution,

the Greek letter "mu," μ, is the mean of the distribution, n is the number of values in the distribution, and the capital Greek letter "sigma," Σ, indicates summing the terms.

1. The shoe lengths, in centimeters, of 10 third grade girls are shown in the table.

22	23	21	24	22	21	19	23	22	20

To compute the standard deviation of this sample of third grade girls' shoe lengths first determine the

mean, μ, of the distribution. $\mu = \dfrac{22 + 23 + \ldots + 22 + 20}{10} = 21.7$ cm.

a. Compute the deviations from the mean, square them, and determine their sums.

Name	x_i	$(x_i - \mu)$	$(x_i - \mu)^2$
Sarah	22	$(22 - 21.7) = 0.3$	$(22 - 21.7)^2 = 0.09$
Carmen	23	$(23 - 21.7) = 1.3$	$(23 - 21.7)^2 = 1.69$
Tina	21	$(21 - 21.7) = -0.7$	$(21 - 21.7)^2 = 0.49$
Mekia	24		
Ky	22		
Michelle	21		
Caroline	19		
Gabby	23		
Shannon	22		
Heather	20		
		$\sum(x_i - \mu) = 0$	$\sum(x_i - \mu)^2 =$ _____

b. Finally, to compute the standard deviation, determine the average squared deviation by dividing by n, and then determine the positive square root.

$\sigma = \sqrt{\dfrac{\sum(x_i - \mu)^2}{n}} =$ _____

This implies that the typical amount that a third grade girl's shoe length deviates from the mean shoe length is about _____ cm.

c. This dotplot displays the 10 shoe lengths from the table and has vertical lines at the mean and at the values that are one standard deviation above and below the mean.

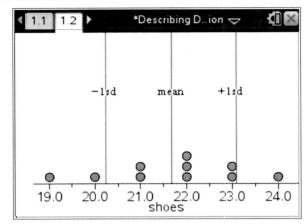

In this distribution, _____ girls' shoe lengths are within one standard deviation of the mean. This means that 70% are within one standard deviation of the _____ shoe length.

d. The deviation for Caroline's shoe length is −2.7 cm. What does this mean in the context of the situation?

e. Carmen's shoe length is less than one standard deviation above the mean. Exactly how many standard deviations above the mean is her shoe length? (Hint: Since standard deviation measures distance from the mean, divide the deviation by the standard deviation, $\frac{x_i - \mu}{\sigma}$.)

2. Consider a group of 8 large dogs that are playing in a local dog park specifically designed for larger breeds. The dogs' weights in pounds are shown in the table.

| 45 | 47 | 55 | 65 | 69 | 70 | 77 | 99 |

a. What is the mean weight of these 8 dogs?

b. Complete the table to determine the sum of the squared deviations from the mean.

x_i	$(x_i - \mu)$	$(x_i - \mu)^2$
45		
47		
55		
65		
69		
70		
77		
99		
	$\sum(x_i - \mu) = 0$	$\sum(x_i - \mu)^2 = $ _____

c. Using the answer from part (b), what is the standard deviation of the weight of these 8 large dogs?

d. The section of the dog park set apart for smaller dogs has 10 dogs playing in it. Their weights are 12, 12.5, 13.5, 14, 17, 20, 21, 21, 22, and 24 pounds. Which group has a larger standard deviation, the large dogs or the small dogs? Why?

e. When the 24-pound dog wanders into the part of the park where the large dogs are playing, the new mean weight of the dogs in the large dog area is 61.222 pounds and the new standard deviation is 20.324 pounds. Why did the mean decrease and the standard deviation increase? Explain the answer.

3. A group of 8 male track athletes is comparing their fastest 400 meter sprint times. Their fastest times are given in the table. Enter the values in one of the lists in your calculator, use the statistics menu, and answer the questions about the sprint times.

Travion	51.053 sec
Tyler	58.230 sec
Michael	57.529 sec
James	55.640 sec
Alex	51.380 sec
Ruben	56.950 sec
Sam	53.559 sec
Teagan	50.909 sec

a. What are the mean and standard deviation of the distribution of the 8 athletes' fastest 400 meter sprint times?

b. Which athletes ran faster than the mean time?

c. How many athletes ran at least one standard deviation faster than the mean? Support the answer with mathematical reasoning.

d. Antonio runs the 400 meter sprint in 52.032 seconds. What are the new mean and standard deviation of times if Antonio's time is included with the other 8 sprinters?

e. Does including Antonio's 400 meter sprint time change the number of runners who ran at least one standard deviation faster than the mean? Explain the answer.

f. Using the new mean and standard deviation, exactly how many standard deviations above the mean is Tyler's time?

4. The tracks for a national car race circuit vary from location to location. The track lengths, in miles, of the 22 tracks are given in the table. Enter the data in a list on your graphing calculator, use the statistics menu, and answer the questions about the track lengths.

1.54	2	0.53	1.5
1.37	2.5	1	1.5
1.5	1.5	1.5	0.53
1.06	1	2.5	0.75
1.5	2.45	1.5	2.66
2	2.5		

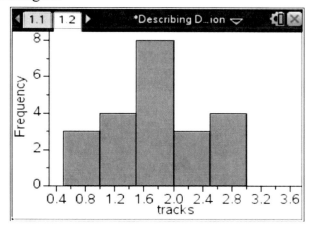

a. What is the mean track length? Draw a vertical line on the histogram showing its approximate value. Explain what this implies in the context of track lengths

b. What percent of the tracks are above the mean? What percent are below the mean?

c. What is the range of the track lengths? Interpret this value in the context of the situation.

d. Using the calculator's statistics menu, what is the standard deviation of the track lengths for this circuit?

e. Draw a vertical line on the graph that is one standard deviation above the mean and another vertical line that is one standard deviation below the mean. How many track lengths are within one standard deviation of the mean? Show the work that leads to the answer.

f. A reporter covering the race circuit asks for a summary of the lengths of the race tracks in the circuit, and you are asked to give the information in a brief description. Write the description using correct statistical language. Be sure to include center (mean, median), shape (skew, mound-shaped, uniform), and variability (standard deviation, range).

5. A local fish and wildlife biologist is studying the effectiveness of a food additive in fish food. She has collected groups of fish into two tanks. Group A is fed the standard fish food. Group B is fed fish food containing the new additive. She weighed all the fish at the start of this study. After two months, she measured the changes in weights, in ounces, of all 24 fish in her study, shown in the table. Enter the data in the lists on your calculator and answer the questions about the fish in her study.

Group A (regular food)		Group B (food additive)	
0.96	1.54	1.52	1.97
1.90	2.35	2.54	2.79
2.63	2.68	3.45	3.52
2.70	2.71	3.59	3.67
3.03	3.17	4.04	4.71
4.07	4.14	5.02	6.37

a. On the graphs provided, draw histograms of the each group with bin widths of one pound.

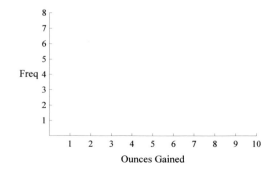

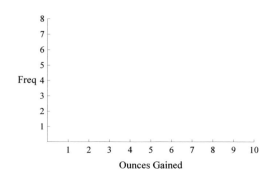

b. What are the mean and standard deviation of the weight gains of the fish in Group A? What are the mean and standard deviation of the weight gains of the fish in Group B?

c. Which group tends to have gained more weight, on average? Explain the answer using mathematical language.

d. Which group seems to have more variability in weight gained? Explain the answer using mathematical language.

e. Does it appear that the food additive is helping fish to gain more weight? Justify your answer using mathematical language.

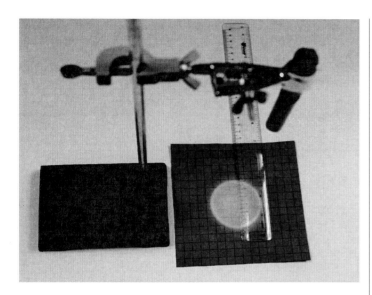

Geometry and Graphical Displays

ABOUT THIS LESSON

This lesson incorporates a wide variety of skills as it connects the concepts of area and volume with graphical displays. Students create boxplots based on class data and interpret boxplots, stemplots, and histograms to determine a geometric shape that could create given data. Two data collection activities that involve a hands-on approach to area and volume are included in the activity.

OBJECTIVES

Students will

- create boxplots.
- interpret boxplots, stemplots, and histograms.
- determine areas and volumes.
- determine measures of center and variability for graphical displays.

LEVEL

Geometry or Math 2 in a unit on areas and volumes

Algebra 2 or Math 3 in a unit on statistics

MODULE/CONNECTIONS TO AP*

Areas and Volumes
Graphical Displays and Distributions

Advanced Placement and AP are registered trademarks of the College Entrance Examination Board. The College Board was not involved in the production of this product.

MODALITY

NMSI emphasizes using multiple representations to connect various approaches to a situation in order to increase student understanding. The lesson provides multiple strategies and models for using those representations indicated by the darkened points of the star to introduce, explore, and reinforce mathematical concepts and to enhance conceptual understanding.

P – Physical
V – Verbal
A – Analytical
N – Numerical
G – Graphical

TEACHER PAGES

COMMON CORE STATE STANDARDS FOR MATHEMATICAL CONTENT

This lesson addresses the following Common Core State Standards for Mathematical Content. The lesson requires that students recall and apply each of these standards rather than providing the initial introduction to the specific skill. The star symbol (*) at the end of a specific standard indicates that the high school standard is connected to modeling.

Targeted Standards

S-IC.1: Understand statistics as a process for making inferences about population parameters based on a random sample from that population.*
See questions 1e, 1h, 2f, 2j, 3d, 4c, 5c

Reinforced/Applied Standards

S-ID.1: Represent data with plots on the real number line (dot plots, histograms, and box plots).*
See questions 1i, 2e, 2i

G-GMD.3: Use volume formulas for cylinders, pyramids, cones, and spheres to solve problems.*
See questions 2g, 2j, 3c, 3d, 4c, 5c, 5e

G-GMD.4: Identify the shapes of two-dimensional cross-sections of three-dimensional objects, and identify three-dimensional objects generated by rotations of two-dimensional objects.
See question 3c

COMMON CORE STATE STANDARDS FOR MATHEMATICAL PRACTICE

These standards describe a variety of instructional practices based on processes and proficiencies that are critical for mathematics instruction. NMSI incorporates these important processes and proficiencies to help students develop knowledge and understanding and to assist them in making important connections across grade levels. This lesson allows teachers to address the following Common Core State Standards for Mathematical Practice.

MP.5: Use appropriate tools strategically.
Students must determine how to set up the data collection process to achieve accurate, consistent results. Students must determine how to secure the flashlight at a correct distance above the desk and how to determine the location of the diameter of the illuminated circle so the results do not vary.

Students must determine which tool (string, ruler, wax-coated string, tape measure) they will use for measurement.

Students use graphing calculators to gather and analyze class data sets for the flashlight and can activities.

MP.6: Attend to precision.
Students determine a process to accurately and consistently measure and collect the data for the flashlight and can activities, using both direct and indirect measurement techniques.

TEACHER PAGES

FOUNDATIONAL SKILLS

The following skills lay the foundation for concepts included in this lesson:

- Use information from a stemplot and a histogram
- Compute the area and circumference of a circle
- Compute the volume of a cone
- Calculate mean, median, mode, and range
- Create a boxplot

ASSESSMENTS

The following formative assessment is embedded in this lesson:

- Students engage in independent practice.

The following additional assessments are located on our website:

- Graphical Displays and Distributions – Geometry Free Response Questions
- Graphical Displays and Distributions – Geometry Multiple Choice Questions
- Graphical Displays and Distributions – Algebra 2 Free Response Questions
- Graphical Displays and Distributions – Algebra 2 Multiple Choice Questions

MATERIALS AND RESOURCES

- Student Activity pages
- Flashlights (LED penlights were used to collect the sample data)
- Yard sticks
- Measuring tapes
- String
- Centimeter rulers
- Cylindrical solids
- Graphing calculators

TEACHING SUGGESTIONS

This lesson contains two data collection activities. Teachers may choose to use either or both of the activities, depending on the available time and resources, to actively engage students in the lesson. Middle grades lessons, such as Stem-and-Leaf Plots, Histograms, and Box-and-Whisker Plots, provide a review of the vocabulary and how to construct these graphs.

For question 1, provide each pair of students with identical flashlights. Students measure and record the diameter of the illuminated circle when holding the flashlight at two different heights. Using the diameter measurement, students calculate the area of the illuminated circle at the different heights and compare the distributions of areas calculated using parallel boxplots. In preparation for this activity, teachers should test the flashlights to ensure that holding the light 30 inches and 33 inches above the surface will produce measurable illuminated circles. Adjust the two heights above the surface as appropriate for the size and intensity of the flashlights that the students will use. For some flashlights, holding the light as low as 6 inches above the surface may be required. Demonstrate the procedure for collecting the data before the students begin to reduce the amount of variability in the data. Ask the students to share ideas on how to hold the flashlight steady and where to measure the diameter of the illuminated circle. As a whole class, decide on a method that everyone will use to collect the data. In part (h), students are asked to approximate the area of the illuminated circle based on the class data. This provides an opportunity to discuss which measure of center is appropriate for the data based on the distribution and can lead to a discussion of how measures of center are applied in the context of a real-world situation.

For question 2, provide a group of 3 or 4 students with a cylindrical object, such as a soup can, that has the same dimensions. Challenge the students to devise a process for measuring the dimensions of the cylindrical object, using a variety of possible tools. Decide on a method as a class so that the collected data is consistent. Ask the students to calculate and record the base area and volume of the solid, based on their measurements. Using the class data, students make conjectures about the actual area and volume of the cylinder based on the distribution of the data from a boxplot. If time is an issue, have students measure a specific can size as homework or provide cans for students to measure the day before.

When collecting the class data, have all of the students display their results from questions 1 and 2 for the class. Students will then enter the class data into their graphing calculator, storing area in L1 and volume in L2 (STAT, Edit). As an alternative to this procedure, have students record their data in one calculator list and link the lists to students' calculators to avoid transcription errors in calculating the one-variable statistics. Use the calculator to determine the five-number summary that students will use to construct their boxplots for both area and volume (STAT, CALC, 1-Var Stats, 2nd 1 (for L1–area) or 2nd 2 (for L2–volume)).

Note: these instructions apply to the TI-83/84 family of graphing calculators. To do this activity with TI-Nspire™ technology, see *Finding the Five-Number Summary of a Data Set* and *Investigating Data Using Box Plots* in the LTF TI-Nspire *Skill Builders*.

Questions 3, 4, and 5 provide additional practice with connecting graphical displays to areas and volumes of geometric figures. Use cooperative groups so that students can discuss the relationship between the mean and median and which measure of center is appropriate.

In question 3c, students graph equations of lines and revolve these about a given axis to form a solid. If this is a new concept for students, complete these questions with the entire class. Additional lessons that address this topic are "Solids of Revolution," a middle grades lesson, and "Volumes of Revolutions," a high school lesson.

A histogram is used in question 5 and is based on the volume of a sphere. Students are asked to work with the formulas for both volume and surface area of this three-dimensional shape.

Suggested modifications for additional scaffolding include the following:

1d   Provide step-by-step instructions for calculating the five-number summary.

1i   Provide a scaled and labeled number line for displaying the parallel boxplots.

2e, 2i Provide a scaled and labeled number line for each boxplot.

3   To reduce data values, modify the stemplot to include volumes greater than 83.0 cm³.

3c   Modify the question to provide the graphs of the three regions.

4a   Provide a method for calculating IQR and range.

4c   Modify the question to provide the student with a list of three sets of dimensions for a rectangle such as $4\,\text{in} \times 6\,\text{in}$, $5\,\text{in} \times 6\,\text{in}$, and $6\,\text{in} \times 6\,\text{in}$. Have the student choose the correct possibility and explain the reasoning.

5c   Modify the question to ask "Calculate the radius of a sphere with a volume of $100\,\text{cm}^3$. Repeat the process with a volume of $128\,\text{cm}^3$. What whole number lies between the two calculated radii?"

5f   Provide $\dfrac{4}{3}\pi r^3 = 4\pi r^2$.

TEACHER PAGES

NMSI CONTENT PROGRESSION CHART

In the spirit of NMSI's goal to connect mathematics across grade levels, a Content Progression Chart for each module demonstrates how specific skills build and develop from sixth grade through pre-calculus in an accelerated program that enables students to take college-level courses in high school, using a faster pace to compress content. In this sequence, Grades 6, 7, 8, and Algebra 1 are compacted into three courses. Grade 6 includes all of the Grade 6 content and some of the content from Grade 7, Grade 7 contains the remainder of the Grade 7 content and some of the content from Grade 8, and Algebra 1 includes the remainder of the content from Grade 8 and all of the Algebra 1 content.

The complete Content Progression Chart for this module is provided on our website and at the beginning of the training manual. This portion of the chart illustrates how the skills included in this particular lesson develop as students advance through this accelerated course sequence.

6th Grade Skills/Objectives	7th Grade Skills/Objectives	Algebra 1 Skills/Objectives	Geometry Skills/Objectives	Algebra 2 Skills/Objectives	Pre-Calculus Skills/Objectives
Create, interpret, and compare dotplots (line plots), stemplots, and bar graphs.	Create, interpret, and compare dotplots (line plots), stemplots, and bar graphs.	Create, interpret, and compare dotplots (line plots), stemplots, and bar graphs.	Create, interpret, and compare dotplots (line plots), stemplots, and bar graphs.	Create, interpret, and compare dotplots (line plots), stemplots, and bar graphs.	Create, interpret, and compare dotplots (line plots), stemplots, and bar graphs.
Calculate the mean, median, mode, range, and mean absolute deviation from tabular or graphical data or data presented in paragraph form.	Calculate the mean, median, mode, range, and mean absolute deviation from tabular or graphical data or data presented in paragraph form.	Calculate the mean, median, mode, range, and standard deviation from tabular or graphical data or data presented in paragraph form.	Calculate the mean, median, mode, range, and standard deviation from tabular or graphical data or data presented in paragraph form.	Calculate the mean, median, mode, range, and standard deviation from tabular or graphical data or data presented in paragraph form	Calculate the mean, median, mode, range, and standard deviation from tabular or graphical data or data presented in paragraph form

TEACHER PAGES

Geometry and Graphical Displays

1. Using a flashlight, a yard stick, and a measuring tape, complete the following investigation with a partner.

    a. Hold the flashlight so that the lens is 30 inches above the table. Measure and record the diameter of the illuminated circle to the nearest tenth of a centimeter.

    b. Calculate the radius using the diameter from part (a).

    c. Calculate the area of the illuminated circle in square centimeters using the radius from part (b). Record the area on a class data table.

    d. Enter the class data for area in a list. From the class data, calculate and record the five-number summary (minimum, Q_1, median, Q_3, and maximum) and the range of the data.

    e. Based on the five-number summary of the class data, approximate the area of the illuminated circle to the nearest square centimeter. Explain your reasoning.

    f. Hold the flashlight at 33 inches above the table and measure the diameter of the illuminated circle to the nearest tenth of a centimeter.

    g. Calculate the area of the illuminated circle in square centimeters and record the result on a class data table. In another list, enter the class data for area of the circle. From the class data, calculate and list the five-number summary (minimum, Q_1, median, Q_3, and maximum) and the range of the data.

    h. Based on the five-number summary of the class data, approximate the area of the circle to the nearest square centimeter. Explain your reasoning.

i. Using the five-number summaries in part (d) and part (g), create parallel boxplots of the class data for area of the flashlight beam.

j. Compare the medians and range in context of the parallel boxplots created in part (i).

2. Complete the following investigation of a cylindrical solid.

a. Determine the circumference of the given cylinder in centimeters.

b. Calculate the radius based on the circumference determined in part (a).

c. Calculate the area of the base of the solid, in square centimeters, using the radius from part (b). Record the area on a class data table.

d. Enter the class data for area in a list. From the class data, calculate and record the five-number summary (minimum, Q_1, median, Q_3, and maximum), the mean, and the range of the data.

e. Using the five-number summary calculated in part (d), create a boxplot to display the distribution of the data for the area.

f. Based on the boxplot of the class data, approximate the area of the base to the nearest square centimeter. Explain your reasoning based on the shape of the boxplot.

g. Measure the height of the cylinder in centimeters and use it to determine the cylinder's volume. Record the volume on a class data table.

h. Enter the class data for volume in another list. From the class data, calculate and record the five-number summary (minimum, Q_1, median, Q_3, and maximum), the mean, and the range of the data.

i. Using the five-number summary from part (h) create a boxplot to display the data distribution for the calculated volumes.

j. Based on the boxplot of the class data, approximate the volume of the solid to the nearest cubic centimeter. Explain your reasoning based on the shape of the boxplot.

3. The science classes in your school have been measuring and recording the volumes of objects of various shapes. The stemplot showing fifty volumes calculated by students displays the distribution of the volume, to the nearest tenth of a cubic centimeter, of a particular solid.

78	8
79	0 3 4 4 7
80	0 3 7 7
81	4 5 7 8 9 9
82	0 1 1 6 6 8 8
83	2 4 7
84	1 3 5 5 5 5 6
85	1 2 2 2 2 4 7 7 7 8 9
86	8 9
87	0
88	2 4 9

Key: **85|2 means 85.2 cubic centimeters**

a. Determine the arithmetic mean, the median, the mode, and the range of the data.

b. Interpret the meaning of the range and median in the context of the situation.

c. Which of the following figures, revolved about the given axis, could have produced the data shown in the stemplot? Use centimeters for the units. Show all the work that leads to the answer.

   i. the region bounded by $x = 0$, $y = 1$, and $y = -\dfrac{5}{4}x + 6$, revolved about the y-axis

   ii. the region bounded by $x = 0$, $y = 0$, and $y = \dfrac{4}{5}x - 4$, revolved about the y-axis

   iii. the region bounded by $x = 0$, $y = 1$, and $y = -\dfrac{4}{5}(x - 5) + 1$, revolved about $y = 1$

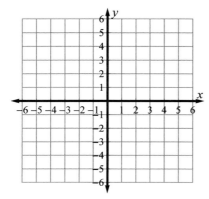 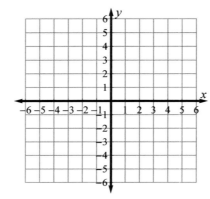 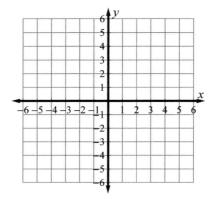

d. Based on the figure(s) you selected in part (c), what is the actual volume? If the dimensions of the shape measured by the science students were the same as your answer in part (c), was the variability (range) in the data collected by the science students reasonable when compared to the actual volume? Explain.

4. Students from several math classes were asked to measure the dimensions of a shape and calculate its area. The boxplot shows the distribution of the area, in square centimeters, based on their measurements.

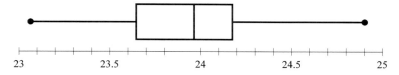

a. The five-number summary from the data is as follows:
   min $= 23.064$; $Q_1 = 23.645$; median $= 23.964$; $Q_3 = 24.174$; max $= 24.902$
   Determine the range and the interquartile range of the data.

b. Can you determine the mean and the mode? Explain.

c. List the dimensions of at least three different geometric shapes that could have generated the data.

5. A group of one hundred students was asked to measure the dimensions of an object and determine its volume. The histogram displays the volumes, in cubic centimeters, that students determined based on their measurements.

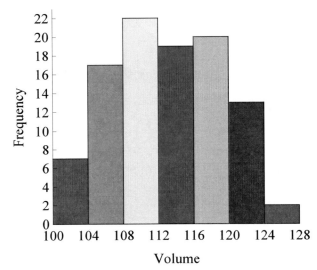

a. Explain the meaning of the first bin, data interval, in the context of the situation.

b. Identify the interval where the median is located. Can you determine the exact value of the median? Explain.

c. The object that the students measured was a sphere. Determine the radius of the sphere, assuming this dimension is a whole number.

d. Use the answer from part (c) to calculate the surface area of the sphere.

e. The surface area and the volume of this sphere have approximately the same numerical values but different units. Use the formulas for volume and surface area of a sphere to determine whether there are other values of r for which the volume and surface area would have the same numerical values.

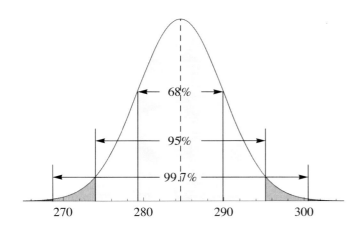

Empirical Rule and Normal Distributions

ABOUT THIS LESSON

In this lesson, students are introduced to the empirical rule and *z*-scores for normal distributions. When only the summary values (mean and standard deviation) are given, students calculate the population percent for the data using *z*-scores and a *z*-table or technology. These probabilities are then used to make a decision for a manufacturing process.

LEVEL

Algebra 2 or Math 3 in a unit on statistics

MODULE/CONNECTION TO AP*

Graphical Displays and Distributions

*Advanced Placement and AP are registered trademarks of the College Entrance Examination Board. The College Board was not involved in the production of this product.

MODALITY

NMSI emphasizes using multiple representations to connect various approaches to a situation in order to increase student understanding. The lesson provides multiple strategies and models for using those representations indicated by the darkened points of the star to introduce, explore, and reinforce mathematical concepts and to enhance conceptual understanding.

OBJECTIVES

Students will

- create a histogram of univariate data.
- use the empirical rule to estimate population percentages.
- calculate a *z*-score and use it to determine population percentages.
- use a *z*-table to estimate areas under the normal curve.
- make decisions based on probabilities.

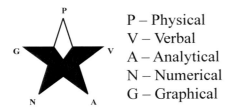

P – Physical
V – Verbal
A – Analytical
N – Numerical
G – Graphical

TEACHER PAGES

COMMON CORE STATE STANDARDS FOR MATHEMATICAL CONTENT

This lesson addresses the following Common Core State Standards for Mathematical Content. The lesson requires that students recall and apply each of these standards rather than providing the initial introduction to the specific skill. The star symbol (*) at the end of a specific standard indicates that the high school standard is connected to modeling.

Targeted Standards

S-ID.4: Use the mean and standard deviation of a data set to fit it to a normal distribution and to estimate population percentages. Recognize that there are data sets for which such a procedure is not appropriate. Use calculators, spreadsheets, and tables to estimate areas under the normal curve.
See questions 1d, 2, 3a-f

S-IC.2: Decide if a specified model is consistent with results from a given data generating process, e.g., using simulation.
For example, a model says a spinning coin falls heads up with probability 0.5. Would a result of 5 tails in a row cause you to question that model?.
See questions 3g-h

Reinforced/Applied Standards

S-ID.2: Use statistics appropriate to the shape of the data distribution to compare center (mean, median) and spread (interquartile range, standard deviation) of two or more different data sets.
See questions 1b-c

S-ID.1: Represent data with plots on the real number line (dot plots, histograms, and box plots).*
See question 1a

COMMON CORE STATE STANDARDS FOR MATHEMATICAL PRACTICE

These standards describe a variety of instructional practices based on processes and proficiencies that are critical for mathematics instruction. NMSI incorporates these important processes and proficiencies to help students develop knowledge and understanding and to assist them in making important connections across grade levels. This lesson allows teachers to address the following Common Core State Standards for Mathematical Practice.

MP.3: Construct viable arguments and critique the reasoning of others.
In questions 3f and 3g, students apply population percentages to explain a decision based on the likelihood of an event.

MP.7: Look for and make use of structure.
Students recognize symmetry of the distribution when determining the population percentage above or below specific values.

TEACHER PAGES

FOUNDATIONAL SKILLS

The following skills lay the foundation for concepts included in this lesson:

- Create graphical displays of data using technology
- Calculate and interpret measures of central tendency
- Calculate a mean and standard deviation of a distribution

ASSESSMENTS

The following types of formative assessments are embedded in this lesson:

- Students engage in independent practice.
- Students summarize a process or procedure.

MATERIALS AND RESOURCES

- Student Activity pages
- Graphing calculators

TEACHER PAGES

TEACHING SUGGESTIONS

Data distributions that have a symmetrical mound shape can be described as having an "approximately normal" distribution. Distributions of this shape have certain properties that allow estimates to be made about the total population percentage having particular values.

In an approximately normal distribution, the empirical rule states that about 68% of the values fall within one standard deviation of the mean, 95% of the values will fall within two standard deviations of the mean, and 99.7% will fall within three standard deviations of the mean. This is helpful information when we may not have all the data but are given only descriptive values.

Students may not be familiar with reading values from the type of table in this lesson. To read the z-table given at the end of the lesson, students use the left hand column for the z-score to the tenths place and the top row of the table for the hundredths place. For example, the population percentage less than a z-score of 1.52 can be read from the table as shown:

z	0.00	0.01	0.02	0.03	0.04
0.0	0.5000	0.5040	0.5080	0.5120	0.5160
0.1	0.5398	0.5438	0.5478	0.5517	0.5557
0.2	0.5793	0.5832	0.5871	0.5910	0.5948
1.3	0.9032	0.9049	0.9066	0.9082	0.9099
1.4	0.9192	0.9207	0.9222	0.9236	0.9251
1.5	0.9332	0.9345	0.9357	0.9370	0.9382

The population percentage of values below a z-score of 1.52 is approximately 93.57 %.

Since 100% of the population is included in the normal curve, to calculate the percent above a z-score of 1.52 standard deviations, subtract 93.57% from 100%. $100\% - 93.57\% = 6.43\%$ of the population have z-scores greater than 1.52.

The percent of a population below a certain value can also be calculated using the graphing calculator. For example, the percent of a population with z-scores below 2.45 can be computed as follows: (syntax and screen shots shown are for TI-83/84 family with the operating system 2.55 MP).

In the distributions menu (2nd, Vars) use the *normalcdf* distribution.

Enter the lower and upper boundary.
Note: since the z-distribution is continuous from $-\infty$ to $+\infty$, a number with large magnitude can be used for the lower bound when looking for values below a certain z-score or for the upper bound when looking for values above a certain z-score.

So for a z-score of 2.45, the population percentage below is *normcdf* $(-1E99, 2.45) \approx .9929$.

The same syntax can be used to determine the percent between two z-scores. For example, the percent between $z = -1.35$ and $z = 1.62$ could be calculated using *normcdf* $(-1.35, 1.62) \approx 0.8589$.

You may wish to support this activity with TI-Nspire™ technology. See *Graphical Representations of Data* in the NMSI TI-Nspire Skill Builders.

Suggested modifications for additional scaffolding include the following:

2a   Set up a process to calculate the values one standard deviation from the mean.

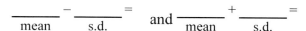

Repeat the process with these answers for the position of 2 standard deviations from the mean. Repeat for 3 standard deviations from the mean.

2d   Provide this model for the student who needs assistance in visualizing the remaining portion of the population when you remove the 68%. Require the student to shade the 68% being removed to visualize the remaining portion to be calculated.

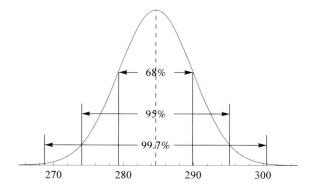

2e   Use a different color to shade the 95% portion of the population. Calculate the portion remaining, and then divide this percentage into the two equal parts.

2f   Provide a graph of the distribution with the mean and standard deviations marked with vertical lines and Michael's weight plotted on the horizontal axis. Provide the student with 4 options from which to choose. For example, options could include 68%, 84%, 95%, and 97.5%.

2k   Provide this model which demonstrates subtracting the areas underneath the curve and determining the area between two values.

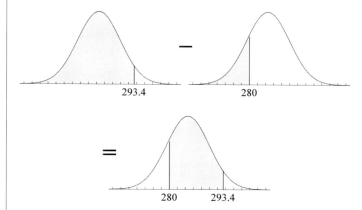

3f   Provide the formula for calculating the probability of a compound event involving two independent events, $P(A \text{ and } B) = P(A) \bullet P(B)$

NMSI CONTENT PROGRESSION CHART

In the spirit of NMSI's goal to connect mathematics across grade levels, a Content Progression Chart for each module demonstrates how specific skills build and develop from sixth grade through pre-calculus in an accelerated program that enables students to take college-level courses in high school, using a faster pace to compress content. In this sequence, Grades 6, 7, 8, and Algebra 1 are compacted into three courses. Grade 6 includes all of the Grade 6 content and some of the content from Grade 7, Grade 7 contains the remainder of the Grade 7 content and some of the content from Grade 8, and Algebra 1 includes the remainder of the content from Grade 8 and all of the Algebra 1 content.

The complete Content Progression Chart for this module is provided on our website and at the beginning of the training manual. This portion of the chart illustrates how the skills included in this particular lesson develop as students advance through this accelerated course sequence.

6th Grade Skills/Objectives	7th Grade Skills/Objectives	Algebra 1 Skills/Objectives	Geometry Skills/Objectives	Algebra 2 Skills/Objectives	Pre-Calculus Skills/Objectives
Create, interpret, and compare dotplots (line plots), stemplots, and bar graphs.	Create, interpret, and compare dotplots (line plots), stemplots, bar graphs, histograms, and boxplots.	Create, interpret, and compare dotplots (line plots), stemplots, bar graphs, histograms, and boxplots.	Create, interpret, and compare dotplots (line plots), stemplots, bar graphs, histograms, and boxplots.	Create, interpret, and compare dotplots (line plots), stemplots, bar graphs, histograms, and boxplots.	Create, interpret, and compare dotplots (line plots), stemplots, bar graphs, histograms, and boxplots.
Calculate the mean, median, mode, range, and mean absolute deviation from tabular or graphical data or data presented in paragraph form.	Calculate the mean, median, mode, range, and mean absolute deviation from tabular or graphical data or data presented in paragraph form.	Calculate the mean, median, mode, range, and standard deviation from tabular or graphical data or data presented in paragraph form..	Calculate the mean, median, mode, range, and standard deviation from tabular or graphical data or data presented in paragraph form.	Calculate the mean, median, mode, range, and standard deviation from tabular or graphical data or data presented in paragraph form.	Calculate the mean, median, mode, range, and standard deviation from tabular or graphical data or data presented in paragraph form.
				Determine population percentages and probability for normal distributions using the empirical rule, tables, and technology.	Determine population percentages and probability for normal distributions using the empirical rule, tables, and technology.

TEACHER PAGES

Empirical Rule and Normal Distributions

Data distributions that have a symmetrical mound shape can be described as having an "approximately normal" distribution. Distributions of this shape have certain properties that allow estimates to be made about the total population percentage having particular values.

1. Consider the distribution of SAT math scores for a group of students.
    504, 542, 544, 568, 568, 573, 575, 577, 578, 585, 599, 603, 609, 610, 628, 645, 655, 670, 679

    a. Draw a histogram of the SAT scores on the graph provided.

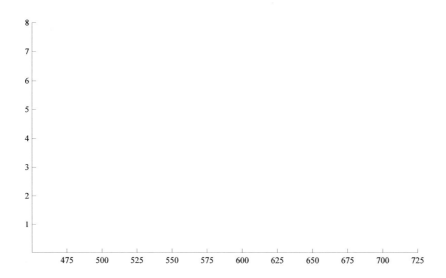

    b. Describe the shape of the distribution of scores.

    c. Determine the mean and standard deviation of this distribution.

    d. What percent of the SAT scores are less than one standard deviation from the mean? Within two standard deviations?

In an approximately normal distribution, the empirical rule states that about 68% of the values fall within one standard deviation of the mean, 95% of the values will fall within two standard deviations of the mean, and 99.7% will fall within three standard deviations of the mean.

2. Consider the distribution of defensive lineman in a professional football league. The mean weight for defensive linemen in the league is 284.6 lbs with a standard deviation of 5.3 lbs, and the distribution is approximately normal.

   a. Draw vertical lines on the sketch of the distribution showing the mean and standard deviations out to ±3 standard deviations. Label the percent of the population within one, two, and three standard deviations.

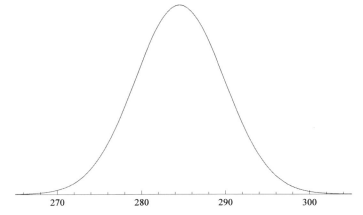

   b. About what percent of defensive linemen in the league weigh between 274 and 295.2 pounds?

   c. Since the distribution of weights is symmetric, the mean and median are equal. What percent of the defensive linemen weigh less than the mean, 284.6 pounds?

   d. About what percent of the defensive linemen weigh less than 279.3 pounds? Use the sketch of the distribution to support your answer.

279.3

e. About what percent of defensive linemen in the league have a weight above 295.2 pounds? Fill in the sketch of the distribution to support your answer.

f. Michael weighs 293.4 pounds. Between _____ percent and _____ percent of the defensive linemen in this league weigh less than Michael.

g. To approximate the percent of linemen that weigh less than Michael, first determine the standardized score or "z-score" of his weight. The z-score is computed using $z = \dfrac{x_i - \mu}{\sigma}$ where x_i represents the value under consideration, μ represents the mean of the data set, and σ represents the standard deviation of the data set. What is Michael's z-score?

h. A table of population percentages below particular z-scores is provided at the end of the lesson. The z-table gives the population percent below a particular z-score if the population distribution is normally distributed. Use the table to determine the approximate percentage of defensive linemen that weigh less than Michael.

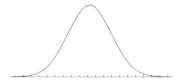

i. What is the z-score for Marcus who weighs 275 pounds?

j. Considering that 100% of the linemen are included in the distribution, what percent of linemen weigh more than Marcus? Fill in the sketch of the distribution to support your answer.

k. What percent of the defensive linemen weigh between 280 and 293.4 pounds? Fill in the sketch of the distribution to support your answer.

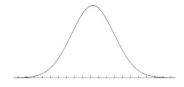

l. If a certain golf cart used to transport injured players is only rated to hold players up to 300 pounds, what percent of the defensive lineman would need a different cart if they were injured?

3. At Fill-er-up Bottling Company, the machines that fill the soda cans are set to put 12 ounces of soda in a can labeled to contain 12 ounces. Due to variability in the filling machines, the actual volume of soda in the 12 ounce cans has an approximately normal distribution with a mean of 12 ounces and a standard deviation of 0.2 ounces.

   a. What percent of soda cans produced by Fill-er-up contain less than the labeled 12 ounces? Use a sketch of the distribution to support your answer.

   b. What percent of the soda cans produced will contain greater than 12.45 ounces of soda? Use a sketch of the distribution to support your answer.

   c. What percent of the soda cans produced will contain between 11.75 and 12.25 ounces of soda? Use a sketch of the distribution to support your answer.

   d. Assuming that the can has a true capacity of 12.6 ounces of soda, how likely is it that a can will be overfilled?

   e. Fill-er-up Bottling Company produces and ships 10,000 cans of soda every day. About how many cans per day should they expect to have at least 12.55 ounces of soda?

   f. Luke is the production manager at Fill-er-up and has just found three cans in a row containing at least 12.55 ounces. Assuming the machine is functioning correctly, what is the probability of 3 cans in a row containing at least 12.55 ounces? Is this outcome likely to happen if the machine is working properly? (Hint: assume the bottles are filled independently of one another)

   g. Based on your answers to part (f), do you think the machine is working properly? Explain your answer.

z	0.00	0.01	0.02	0.03	0.04	0.05	0.06	0.07	0.08	0.09
-3.0	0.0013	0.0013	0.0013	0.0012	0.0012	0.0011	0.0011	0.0011	0.0010	0.0010
-2.9	0.0019	0.0018	0.0018	0.0017	0.0016	0.0016	0.0015	0.0015	0.0014	0.0014
-2.8	0.0026	0.0025	0.0024	0.0023	0.0023	0.0022	0.0021	0.0021	0.0020	0.0019
-2.7	0.0035	0.0034	0.0033	0.0032	0.0031	0.0030	0.0029	0.0028	0.0027	0.0026
-2.6	0.0047	0.0045	0.0044	0.0043	0.0041	0.0040	0.0039	0.0038	0.0037	0.0036
-2.5	0.0062	0.0060	0.0059	0.0057	0.0055	0.0054	0.0052	0.0051	0.0049	0.0048
-2.4	0.0082	0.0080	0.0078	0.0075	0.0073	0.0071	0.0069	0.0068	0.0066	0.0064
-2.3	0.0107	0.0104	0.0102	0.0099	0.0096	0.0094	0.0091	0.0089	0.0087	0.0084
-2.2	0.0139	0.0136	0.0132	0.0129	0.0125	0.0122	0.0119	0.0116	0.0113	0.0110
-2.1	0.0179	0.0174	0.0170	0.0166	0.0162	0.0158	0.0154	0.0150	0.0146	0.0143
-2.0	0.0228	0.0222	0.0217	0.0212	0.0207	0.0202	0.0197	0.0192	0.0188	0.0183
-1.9	0.0287	0.0281	0.0274	0.0268	0.0262	0.0256	0.0250	0.0244	0.0239	0.0233
-1.8	0.0359	0.0351	0.0344	0.0336	0.0329	0.0322	0.0314	0.0307	0.0301	0.0294
-1.7	0.0446	0.0436	0.0427	0.0418	0.0409	0.0401	0.0392	0.0384	0.0375	0.0367
-1.6	0.0548	0.0537	0.0526	0.0516	0.0505	0.0495	0.0485	0.0475	0.0465	0.0455
-1.5	0.0668	0.0655	0.0643	0.0630	0.0618	0.0606	0.0594	0.0582	0.0571	0.0559
-1.4	0.0808	0.0793	0.0778	0.0764	0.0749	0.0735	0.0721	0.0708	0.0694	0.0681
-1.3	0.0968	0.0951	0.0934	0.0918	0.0901	0.0885	0.0869	0.0853	0.0838	0.0823
-1.2	0.1151	0.1131	0.1112	0.1093	0.1075	0.1056	0.1038	0.1020	0.1003	0.0985
-1.1	0.1357	0.1335	0.1314	0.1292	0.1271	0.1251	0.1230	0.1210	0.1190	0.1170
-1.0	0.1587	0.1562	0.1539	0.1515	0.1492	0.1469	0.1446	0.1423	0.1401	0.1379
-0.9	0.1841	0.1814	0.1788	0.1762	0.1736	0.1711	0.1685	0.1660	0.1635	0.1611
-0.8	0.2119	0.2090	0.2061	0.2033	0.2005	0.1977	0.1949	0.1922	0.1894	0.1867
-0.7	0.2420	0.2389	0.2358	0.2327	0.2296	0.2266	0.2236	0.2206	0.2177	0.2148
-0.6	0.2743	0.2709	0.2676	0.2643	0.2611	0.2578	0.2546	0.2514	0.2483	0.2451
-0.5	0.3085	0.3050	0.3015	0.2981	0.2946	0.2912	0.2877	0.2843	0.2810	0.2776
-0.4	0.3446	0.3409	0.3372	0.3336	0.3300	0.3264	0.3228	0.3192	0.3156	0.3121
-0.3	0.3821	0.3783	0.3745	0.3707	0.3669	0.3632	0.3594	0.3557	0.3520	0.3483
-0.2	0.4207	0.4168	0.4129	0.4090	0.4052	0.4013	0.3974	0.3936	0.3897	0.3859
-0.1	0.4602	0.4562	0.4522	0.4483	0.4443	0.4404	0.4364	0.4325	0.4286	0.4247
0.0	0.5000	0.4960	0.4920	0.4880	0.4840	0.4801	0.4761	0.4721	0.4681	0.4641

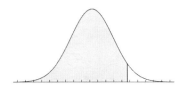

z	0.00	0.01	0.02	0.03	0.04	0.05	0.06	0.07	0.08	0.09
0.0	0.5000	0.5040	0.5080	0.5120	0.5160	0.5199	0.5239	0.5279	0.5319	0.5359
0.1	0.5398	0.5438	0.5478	0.5517	0.5557	0.5596	0.5636	0.5675	0.5714	0.5753
0.2	0.5793	0.5832	0.5871	0.5910	0.5948	0.5987	0.6026	0.6064	0.6103	0.6141
0.3	0.6179	0.6217	0.6255	0.6293	0.6331	0.6368	0.6406	0.6443	0.6480	0.6517
0.4	0.6554	0.6591	0.6628	0.6664	0.6700	0.6736	0.6772	0.6808	0.6844	0.6879
0.5	0.6915	0.6950	0.6985	0.7019	0.7054	0.7088	0.7123	0.7157	0.7190	0.7224
0.6	0.7257	0.7291	0.7324	0.7357	0.7389	0.7422	0.7454	0.7486	0.7517	0.7549
0.7	0.7580	0.7611	0.7642	0.7673	0.7704	0.7734	0.7764	0.7794	0.7823	0.7852
0.8	0.7881	0.7910	0.7939	0.7967	0.7995	0.8023	0.8051	0.8078	0.8106	0.8133
0.9	0.8159	0.8186	0.8212	0.8238	0.8264	0.8289	0.8315	0.8340	0.8365	0.8389
1.0	0.8413	0.8438	0.8461	0.8485	0.8508	0.8531	0.8554	0.8577	0.8599	0.8621
1.1	0.8643	0.8665	0.8686	0.8708	0.8729	0.8749	0.8770	0.8790	0.8810	0.8830
1.2	0.8849	0.8869	0.8888	0.8907	0.8925	0.8944	0.8962	0.8980	0.8997	0.9015
1.3	0.9032	0.9049	0.9066	0.9082	0.9099	0.9115	0.9131	0.9147	0.9162	0.9177
1.4	0.9192	0.9207	0.9222	0.9236	0.9251	0.9265	0.9279	0.9292	0.9306	0.9319
1.5	0.9332	0.9345	0.9357	0.9370	0.9382	0.9394	0.9406	0.9418	0.9429	0.9441
1.6	0.9452	0.9463	0.9474	0.9484	0.9495	0.9505	0.9515	0.9525	0.9535	0.9545
1.7	0.9554	0.9564	0.9573	0.9582	0.9591	0.9599	0.9608	0.9616	0.9625	0.9633
1.8	0.9641	0.9649	0.9656	0.9664	0.9671	0.9678	0.9686	0.9693	0.9699	0.9706
1.9	0.9713	0.9719	0.9726	0.9732	0.9738	0.9744	0.9750	0.9756	0.9761	0.9767
2.0	0.9772	0.9778	0.9783	0.9788	0.9793	0.9798	0.9803	0.9808	0.9812	0.9817
2.1	0.9821	0.9826	0.9830	0.9834	0.9838	0.9842	0.9846	0.9850	0.9854	0.9857
2.2	0.9861	0.9864	0.9868	0.9871	0.9875	0.9878	0.9881	0.9884	0.9887	0.9890
2.3	0.9893	0.9896	0.9898	0.9901	0.9904	0.9906	0.9909	0.9911	0.9913	0.9916
2.4	0.9918	0.9920	0.9922	0.9925	0.9927	0.9929	0.9931	0.9932	0.9934	0.9936
2.5	0.9938	0.9940	0.9941	0.9943	0.9945	0.9946	0.9948	0.9949	0.9951	0.9952
2.6	0.9953	0.9955	0.9956	0.9957	0.9959	0.9960	0.9961	0.9962	0.9963	0.9964
2.7	0.9965	0.9966	0.9967	0.9968	0.9969	0.9970	0.9971	0.9972	0.9973	0.9974
2.8	0.9974	0.9975	0.9976	0.9977	0.9977	0.9978	0.9979	0.9979	0.9980	0.9981
2.9	0.9981	0.9982	0.9982	0.9983	0.9984	0.9984	0.9985	0.9985	0.9986	0.9986
3.0	0.9987	0.9987	0.9987	0.9988	0.9988	0.9989	0.9989	0.9989	0.9990	0.9990

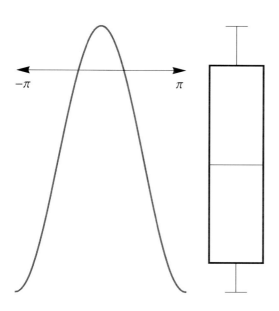

Analyzing Trigonometric Functions Using Graphical Displays

ABOUT THIS LESSON

This lesson incorporates graphical displays with analysis of functions. Students investigate transformations of trigonometric functions using summary statistics and graphical displays of function values. Students will also create histograms and boxplots of function values over fixed domains of trigonometric functions. As a concluding activity, students predict equations of functions based on the shape of the distribution of function values and, conversely, predict distributions of function values based on equations of functions.

OBJECTIVES
Students will
- create and interpret boxplots and histograms.
- evaluate the behavior of function values on restricted domains.
- sketch histograms based on function behavior.
- write a possible trigonometric function on a restricted domain based on a boxplot.

LEVEL
Algebra 2, Math 3, Pre-Calculus, or Math 4 in a unit on graphing trigonometric functions

MODULE/CONNECTION TO AP*
Analysis of Functions
Graphical Displays and Distributions

Advanced Placement and AP are registered trademarks of the College Entrance Examination Board. The College Board was not involved in the production of this product.

MODALITY:
NMSI emphasizes using multiple representations to connect various approaches to a situation in order to increase student understanding. The lesson provides multiple strategies and models for using those representations indicated by the darkened points of the star to introduce, explore, and reinforce mathematical concepts and to enhance conceptual understanding.

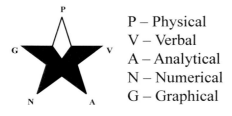

P – Physical
V – Verbal
A – Analytical
N – Numerical
G – Graphical

TEACHER PAGES

COMMON CORE STATE STANDARDS FOR MATHEMATICAL CONTENT

This lesson addresses the following Common Core State Standards for Mathematical Content. The lesson requires that students recall and apply each of these standards rather than providing the initial introduction to the specific skill. The star symbol (*) at the end of a specific standard indicates that the high school standard is connected to modeling.

Targeted Standards

F-BF.3: Identify the effect on the graph of replacing $f(x)$ by $f(x) + k$, $k\,f(x)$, $f(kx)$, and $f(x + k)$ for specific values of k (both positive and negative); find the value of k given the graphs. Experiment with cases and illustrate an explanation of the effects on the graph using technology. *Include recognizing even and odd functions from their graphs and algebraic expressions for them.*
See questions 2c, 3-5

S-ID.3: Interpret differences in shape, center, and spread in the context of the data sets, accounting for possible effects of extreme data points (outliers).*
See questions 2d, 4-5

Reinforced/Applied Standards

S-ID.1: Represent data with plots on the real number line (dot plots, histograms, and box plots).*
See questions 1e, 2b, 2d, 4

F-TF.5: Choose trigonometric functions to model periodic phenomena with specified amplitude, frequency, and midline.*
See question 5

F-IF.7e: Graph functions expressed symbolically and show key features of the graph, by hand in simple cases and using technology for more complicated cases. * (e) Graph exponential and logarithmic functions, showing intercepts and end behavior, and trigonometric functions, showing period, midline, and amplitude.
See questions 1a, 2c

TEACHER PAGES

COMMON CORE STATE STANDARDS FOR MATHEMATICAL PRACTICE

These standards describe a variety of instructional practices based on processes and proficiencies that are critical for mathematics instruction. NMSI incorporates these important processes and proficiencies to help students develop knowledge and understanding and to assist them in making important connections across grade levels. This lesson allows teachers to address the following Common Core State Standards for Mathematical Practice.

MP.1: Make sense of problems and persevere in solving them.
Students make connections between two seemingly unrelated topics, univariate data and trigonometric functions, by using the five-number summary to describe the range values or by creating a histogram of the range values of translated trigonometric functions.

MP.2: Reason abstractly and quantitatively.
Students use their knowledge of transformations of trigonometric functions to predict the five-number summary for a large set of function values.

Students apply their knowledge of boxplots and transformations to write the equations of transformed functions and compare their graphs.

MP.5: Use appropriate tools strategically.
Students use a graphing calculator to generate large sets of random domain values, to evaluate those values in particular functions, and to create a boxplot and histogram of the range values.

FOUNDATIONAL SKILLS

The following skills lay the foundation for concepts included in this lesson:
- Write trigonometric functions given an amplitude, frequency, and midline
- Determine measures of central tendency and variability of data
- Create graphical displays of data

ASSESSMENTS

The following formative assessment is embedded in this lesson:
- Students engage in independent practice.

The following additional assessments are located on our website:
- Graphical Displays and Distributions – Algebra 2 Free Response Questions
- Graphical Displays and Distributions – Algebra 2 Multiple Choice Questions
- Graphical Displays and Distributions – Pre-Calculus Free Response Questions
- Graphical Displays and Distributions – Pre-Calculus Multiple Choice Questions

MATERIALS AND RESOURCES

- Student Activity pages
- Graphing calculators
- NMSI video clip on random domain generation on the TI-84
- NMSI video clip on creating histograms on the TI-84

TEACHER PAGES

TEACHING SUGGESTIONS

A review of histograms, boxplots, shapes of distributions, and measures of center may be helpful before beginning this lesson.

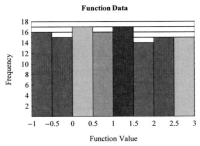

The histogram above would be described as uniform since the bins have the same or similar frequencies throughout the distribution. Since this distribution is fairly symmetric, we expect the mean and median function values to be approximately the same.

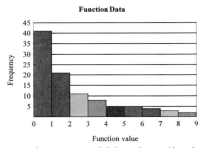

The histogram above would be described as skewed right or skewed to the larger numbers since the tail of the distribution is on the right hand side. Since this distribution is skewed right, the mean function value will typically be larger than the median.

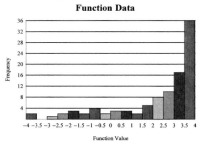

The histogram above would be described as skewed left or skewed to the smaller numbers since the tail of the distribution is on the left hand side. Since this distribution is skewed left, the mean function value will typically be less than the median.

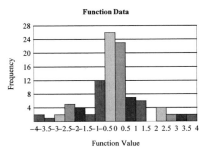

The histogram above would be described as mound shaped. Since the distribution is approximately symmetric, we expect the mean and median function values to be approximately the same.

To assist students to make the connection between the vertical translation on the graph of a function and the horizontal shift of the graphical display of function values, rotate the graphical display 90 degrees to allow for the vertical translation on the function graph to correspond with the translation along the number line in the graphical display. Students may need to compute a few function values by hand to recognize the translations.

The calculator instructions for generating the domain values at random are provided on the last page of the student activity. Discuss the meaning of the syntax of the calculator key strokes when generating the random numbers over the limited domains.

Memory errors may occasionally occur when generating large lists of random numbers since these lists take large amounts of RAM. If memory errors occur, instruct students to clear the lists prior to generating random numbers.

You may wish to support this activity with TI-Nspire™ technology. See *Generating Random Numbers, Graphical Representations of Data*, and *Finding the Five-Number Summary for a Data Set* in the NMSI TI-Nspire Skill Builders.

TEACHER PAGES

Suggested modifications for additional scaffolding include the following:

1c   Provide a written formula for calculating the interquartile range, IQR = $Q_3 - Q_1$

1d   Provide a written formula for calculating outliers,

$$LB = Q_1 - 1.5(\text{IQR}) \quad UB = Q_3 + 1.5(\text{IQR})$$

1e   Provide a scaled number line

2a   Provide a graph of the original function

4   Provide a graph of each function

5   Provide three answer choices to match with the given boxplots.

$$f(x) = \frac{3}{2}\sin(x) + 1, \; \left[0, 2\pi\right]$$

$$g(x) = \frac{3}{4}\sin(x) - 3, \; \left[0, 2\pi\right]$$

$$h(x) = 4\sin(x) + \frac{1}{4}, \; \left[0, 2\pi\right]$$

TEACHER PAGES

NMSI CONTENT PROGRESSION CHART

In the spirit of NMSI's goal to connect mathematics across grade levels, a Content Progression Chart for each module demonstrates how specific skills build and develop from sixth grade through pre-calculus in an accelerated program that enables students to take college-level courses in high school, using a faster pace to compress content. In this sequence, Grades 6, 7, 8, and Algebra 1 are compacted into three courses. Grade 6 includes all of the Grade 6 content and some of the content from Grade 7, Grade 7 contains the remainder of the Grade 7 content and some of the content from Grade 8, and Algebra 1 includes the remainder of the content from Grade 8 and all of the Algebra 1 content.

The complete Content Progression Chart for this module is provided on our website and at the beginning of the training manual. This portion of the chart illustrates how the skills included in this particular lesson develop as students advance through this accelerated course sequence.

6th Grade Skills/Objectives	7th Grade Skills/Objectives	Algebra 1 Skills/Objectives	Geometry Skills/Objectives	Algebra 2 Skills/Objectives	Pre-Calculus Skills/Objectives
Create, interpret, and compare dotplots (line plots), stemplots, and bar graphs.	Create, interpret, and compare dotplots (line plots), stemplots, bar graphs, histograms, and boxplots.	Create, interpret, and compare dotplots (line plots), stemplots, bar graphs, histograms, and boxplots.	Create, interpret, and compare dotplots (line plots), stemplots, bar graphs, histograms, and boxplots.	Create, interpret, and compare dotplots (line plots), stemplots, bar graphs, histograms, and boxplots.	Create, interpret, and compare dotplots (line plots), stemplots, bar graphs, histograms, and boxplots.
Calculate the mean, median, mode, range, and mean absolute deviation from tabular or graphical data or data presented in paragraph form.	Calculate the mean, median, mode, range, and mean absolute deviation from tabular or graphical data or data presented in paragraph form.	Calculate the mean, median, mode, range, and standard deviation from tabular or graphical data or data presented in paragraph form.	Calculate the mean, median, mode, range, and standard deviation from tabular or graphical data or data presented in paragraph form.	Calculate the mean, median, mode, range, and standard deviation from tabular or graphical data or data presented in paragraph form	Calculate the mean, median, mode, range, and standard deviation from tabular or graphical data or data presented in paragraph form

TEACHER PAGES

Analyzing Trigonometric Functions Using Graphical Displays

1. Consider $f(x) = \sin(x)$

   a. Sketch $f(x)$ on the interval $[0, 2\pi]$.

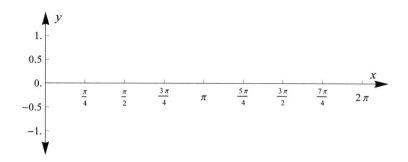

   b. Randomly select 100 domain values following the instructions at the end of the lesson, and evaluate $f(x)$ at each of those function values. Generate a five-number summary of the function values.

   c. Determine the IQR and range.

   d. Based on your answers in parts (b) and (c), are there any outliers? Show the calculations that lead to your answer.

e. Draw a boxplot based on the five-number summary calculated in (b). Display any outliers calculated in part (d).

2. Select 100 domain values at random from the interval $\left[-\pi, \pi\right]$ and evaluate the function $g(x) = 3\cos(x) - 2$.

a. Generate the five-number summary for the function values.

b. Draw and label a boxplot using the summary statistics in part (a). Show outliers if any exist.

c. Sketch the function $g(x) = 3\cos(x) - 2$ from $\left[-\pi, \pi\right]$.

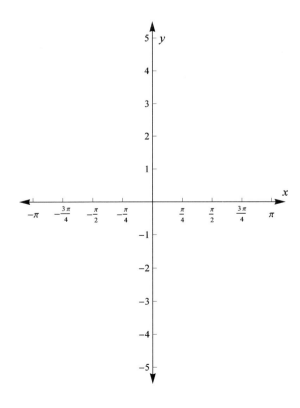

d. Using the same data, generate a histogram with bin widths of 0.5. Sketch the histogram on the graph provided and then re-draw the boxplot directly below the function value axis.

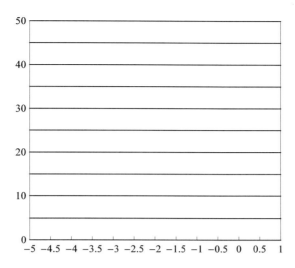

How is the shape of the histogram related to the location of the median function value? How is the length of the "whiskers" of the boxplot related to the frequency of the associated bins of the histogram?

3. When evaluated over the interval $[0, 2\pi]$, $f(x) = 2\cos(x)$ has a five-number summary: $-2, -1.5, 0, 1.5, 2$. Predict the five-number summary for each of the following transformations of $f(x)$ over the same interval.

a. $g(x) = f(x) - 3$

b. $h(x) = -f(x) + 3$

c. $i(x) = 3f(x) - 4$

4. Match each of the following trigonometric functions with one boxplot and one histogram of function values.

a. _____;_____ $f(x) = \frac{1}{2}\cos(x) + 2$ $[0, 2\pi]$	I. 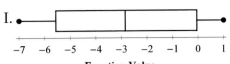	i. 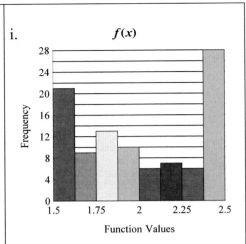
b. _____;_____ $f(x) = 4\sin(x) - 3$ $[-2\pi, 2\pi]$	II. 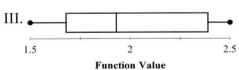	ii. 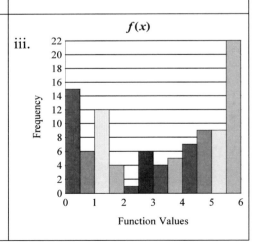
c. _____;_____ $f(x) = -3\sin(x) + 3$ $[-\pi, \pi]$	III.	iii.

5. For each of the boxplots, state a possible trigonometric function on a restricted domain.

a.

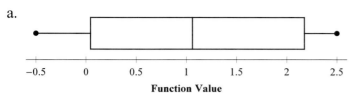

b.

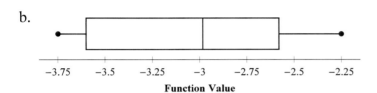

c.

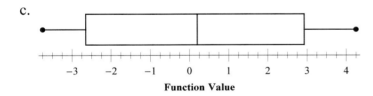

In order to ensure that all groups will generate different random numbers, seed the graphing calculators by storing the last four digits of a phone number in rand on the graphing calculator.

The key sequence is as follows:
Step 1: Students enter the last four digits of their phone numbers
Step 2: Press STO▸
Step 3: Press MATH, arrow over to PRB, press 1
Step 4: Press ENTER and the new number is the seed for the random number generator

To generate a large quantity of random numbers at one time over a limited domain and store these values in List 1 on the calculator, use the following steps:

Step 1: Enter the width of the domain
Step 2: Press MATH, arrow over to PRB, press 1
Step 3: Press (, enter the number of random values required, press)
Step 4: Press +, enter the smallest value in the domain
Step 5: Press STO▸, 2nd, 1

The syntax is W*rand(n)+A á L1 where W is the width of the domain, A is the smallest value in the domain, and n is the number of values you want to generate.

For example to generate 100 random values on the domain $\left[-2, 6\right]$ on the calculator, the display would be:

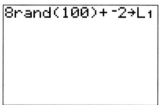

To evaluate a function that is in Y1 at the values in a list, use the following steps:
Step 1: Press STAT, press 1, arrow to the header of L2 and press CLEAR, press ENTER
Step 2: Arrow to the header of L2, press VARS, arrow to [Y-VARS], press 1, press 1
Step 3: Press (, 2nd, 1,) then press ENTER

The calculator display would be:

L1	L2	L3	2
3.038	------	------	
2.9915			
3.0115			
3.016			
3.0568			
3.04			
2.913			
L2 =Y₁(L₁)			

Introduction to the NMSI Mathematics Multiple Choice Quizzes

The National Math and Science Initiative multiple choice questions are modeled after multiple choice questions on the AP* Calculus and Statistics exams. The questions are assigned a course-level designation based on an accelerated program that enables students to take college-level courses in high school, using a faster pace to compress content. In this sequence, Grades 6, 7, 8, and Algebra 1 are compacted into three courses. Grade 6 includes all of the Grade 6 content and some of the content from Grade 7, Grade 7 contains the remainder of the Grade 7 content and some of the content from Grade 8, and Algebra 1 includes the remainder of the content from Grade 8 and all of the Algebra 1 content.

The grade-level multiple choice quizzes for sixth grade through pre-calculus assess the skills and concepts introduced in each module. These quizzes reflect the module's Content Progression Chart, which outlines the mathematics imbedded in the activities for each grade level, and the Concept Development Chart, which provides examples of how those concepts or skills might be assessed. Additionally, the quizzes are directly linked to the NMSI posttests for each grade level. Once students have completed the activities, teachers may use the quiz questions to determine student understanding and to prepare students for the level of rigor on the posttests.

When scoring the multiple choice questions, teachers should remember that the quizzes are intended to model the rigor of questioning on AP exams. A suggested scoring guideline, which is also included with the rationales for each quiz, is:

Percent Correct	Grade
0 – 29	50
30 – 49	60
50 – 59	70
60 – 69	80
70 – 79	90
80 – 100	100

All of these materials – lessons and activities with answer keys, grade-level quizzes with rationales, and free response questions with scoring rubrics and student samples – are available for each module on the NMSI website.

Sample Quiz Questions

1. 6th Grade Module 3 Question 6:

    Samantha wants to buy her mom a pair of earrings for her birthday. She searched an internet site for the prices of earrings she thought her mom might like. The table represents the price list from the website.

Earrings	Earring Prices
Brand A	$9.50
Brand B	$12.50
Brand C	$25.00
Brand D	$16.25
Brand E	$10.50

    What is the median price?

    A. $12.50

    B. $14.75

    C. $15.50

    D. $17.25

    E. $25.00

2. 6th Grade Module 3 Question 7

    The website is offering a sale price of 20% off the earrings that cost $25.00. Which of the following describes how the range of the prices changes with this sale?

    A. The range increases by $5.00.

    B. The range increases by $1.00

    C. The range does not change.

    D. The range decreases by $5.00.

    E. The range decreases by $0.50.

3.   7th Grade Module 3 Question 5
Myrna is researching the amount of sugar in popular soft drinks. If a soft drink has 40 grams of sugar, this means that there are 10 teaspoons of sugar in the drink. According to a website, 3 drinks contain at least 6 grams of sugar but less than 16 grams, 4 drinks contain at least 16 grams of sugar but less than 26 grams, and 7 contain at least 26 grams but less than 36 grams of sugar. There are 17 soft drinks that contain greater than 36 grams of sugar but less than 46 grams and 9 drinks with at least 46 grams but less than 56 grams of sugar.

Which histogram correctly displays the data?

A.
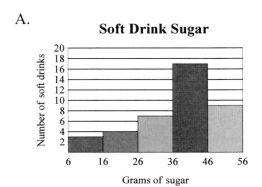

B.
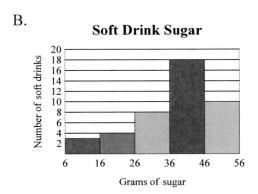

C.
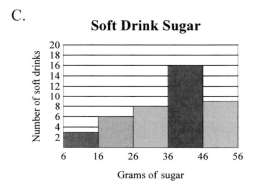

D.
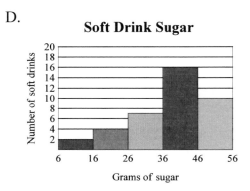

E.
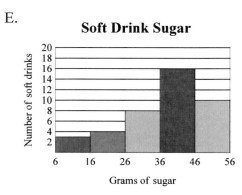

4. 7th Grade Module 3 Question 8 (Calculator Allowed)

The modern Olympic Games, which were first held in 1896, are scheduled every four years. The table displays the winning times for the men's 100 meter dash for five Olympic Games from 1988 to 2004.

Year	Winning Time (in seconds) for Men's 100 Meter Dash
1988	9.92
1992	9.96
1996	9.84
2000	9.87
2004	9.85

In 2008 the winning time for the men's 100 meter dash was 9.72 seconds. How will the median change if the 2008 time is included with the data in the table? Round the answer to the nearest hundredth.

A. Increase by 0.03 seconds

B. Increase by 0.01 seconds

C. The median does not change

D. Decrease by 0.03 seconds

E. Decrease by 0.01 seconds

5. Algebra 1 Module 3 Question 3
    The histogram shows the distribution of the salaries, rounded to the nearest million dollars, for the highest paid professional football players.

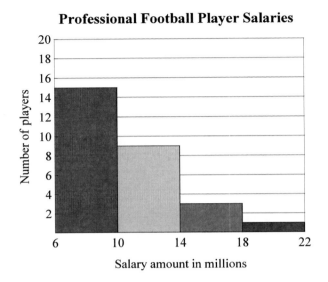

Based on the graph, in which bin is the median salary for the football players located?

A. $\$6,000,000 \leq$ salary $< \$10,000,000$

B. $\$10,000,000 \leq$ salary $< \$14,000,000$

C. $\$14,000,000 \leq$ salary $< \$18,000,000$

D. $\$18,000,000 \leq$ salary $< \$22,000,000$

E. There is not enough information to determine the location of the median.

6. Algebra 1 Module 3 Question 7
    A popular consumer reporting magazine asked consumers to rate peanut butter on a scale of
    0 to 100. The parallel boxplots display the results of the survey.

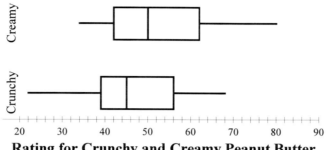

Rating for Crunchy and Creamy Peanut Butter

Which of the following <u>cannot</u> be determined from the boxplots?

A. The ranges for both types of peanut butter are equal.

B. The maximum rating for the creamy peanut butter is not an outlier.

C. Twenty-five percent of the ratings for crunchy peanut butter are between 56 and 68.

D. There were a total of 40 responses for the ratings for creamy peanut butter.

E. Both arithmetic means will be slightly larger than the medians, based on the shapes of
   the graphs.

7. Geometry Module 3 Question 2
    The students enjoyed the first activity so much that the teacher decided to give them another shape to measure and to calculate area. The given histogram displays the class data.

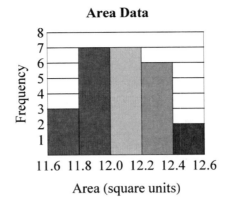

Area Data

Which of the following shapes could have been used by the students?

I. 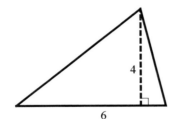   II.    III.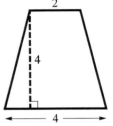

A. I only

B. II only

C. III only

D. I and III only

E. I, II, and III

8. Geometry Module 3 Question 3
    Based on the histogram provided in the previous question, which of the following statements is <u>not</u> true?

A. The arithmetic mean area cannot be calculated from the graph.

B. The range of the data can be determined from the graph.

C. The median is located in the interval, 12.0 square units $\leq$ area < 12.2 square units.

D. The upper quartile is located in the interval, 12.2 square units $\leq$ area < 12.4 square units

E. The mean and median will have approximately the same value since the shape of the graph is somewhat symmetrical.

9. Algebra 2 Module 3 Question 2

    As a project, students were asked to produce a histogram based on a function of their choice. Marty selected the function $f(x) = -3(x-2)^2 + 4$ with a domain of $0 \leq x \leq 3$. Using a graphing calculator, he stored a set of 100 random x-values in the interval $0 \leq x \leq 3$ into a list and then calculated the y-values for each of the random x-values.

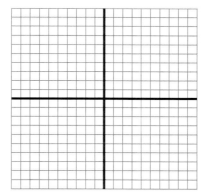

Which of the following histograms could illustrate Marty's data?

A.

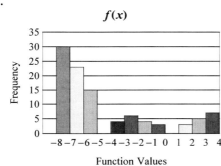

B.

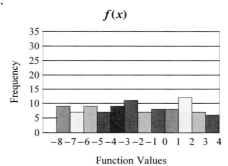

C.

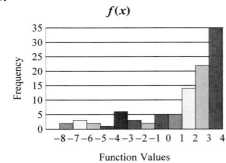

D.

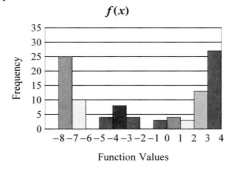

E.

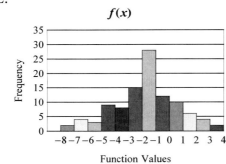

10. Algebra 2 Module 3 Question 3

    Mrs. Brown assigned a function to each student and instructed the students to randomly collect 100 x-values in the domain, $5 \leq x \leq 50$, to calculate the corresponding y-values for the assigned function, and then to construct a boxplot of the y-values. Mason's boxplot is given.

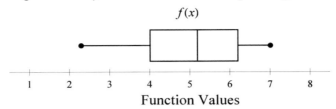

Function Values

Which is the most likely parent function for this boxplot?

A. $f(x) = x^2$

B. $f(x) = x^3$

C. $f(x) = \sqrt{x}$

D. $f(x) = \sqrt[3]{x}$

E. $f(x) = \ln x$

11. Pre-Calculus Module 3 Question 2

One hundred values for *x* were selected randomly from a domain of $[-1, 2.3]$. Which histogram is most likely to display the *y*-values for the function $f(x) = x^3$?

A.

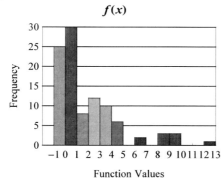

B.

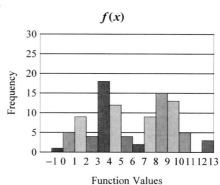

C.

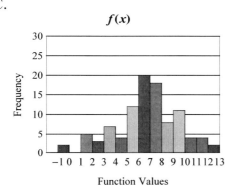

D.

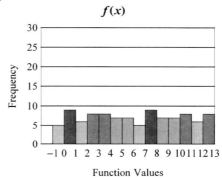

E.

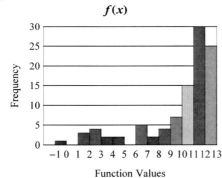

12. Pre-Calculus Module 3 Question 4 (Calculator Allowed)

    Jennifer's class was asked to randomly select 100 x-values on the interval $-2\pi \le x \le 2\pi$ and to generate the corresponding y-values for a particular sinusoidal function, $s(x)$. Using her graphing calculator, Jennifer used the class's 100 y-values from the sinusoidal function and generated the following five number summary:

    $$\text{Min} = -5.999;\ Q_1 = -5.514;\ \text{Med} = -3.543;\ Q_3 = -2.399;\ \text{Max} = -2.$$

    Which of the following functions could the class have used to obtain this data?

    A. $s(x) = \cos(4x) - 2$

    B. $s(x) = 2\cos(x) - 4$

    C. $s(x) = 2\cos(x - 4)$

    D. $s(x) = 4\cos(x) - 2$

    E. $s(x) = 4\cos(x - 2)$

Selected Rationales

3. 7th Grade Module 3 Question 5

    A. Correct. Student selects the histogram where the bins are correct.

    B. Student selects the histogram where the first three bins are correct.

    C. Student selects the histogram where the first bin is correct.

    D. Student selects the histogram where the second and third bins are correct.

    E. Student selects the histogram where the first and last bins are correct.

5. Algebra 1 Module 3 Question 3

    A. Correct. Student determines that the median will be between the fourteenth and fifteenth terms.

    B. Student selects this bin for the location of the median or selects a bin that displays 14 since it is the median of the scale.

    C. Student selects this bin for the location of the median or selects a bin that contains 14 since it is the median of the scale.

    D. Student selects this bin for the location of the median.

    E. Student does not understand how to determine the location of the median.

7. Geometry Module 3 Question 2

    I. True. The area is 12 square units, so the variation in measurement for this shape could generate the data displayed in the histogram.

    II. False. The area is 8 square units, so the variation in measurement for this shape would not generate the data displayed in the histogram.

    III. True. The area is 12 square units, so the variation in measurement for this shape could generate the data displayed in the histogram.

    A. Student selects the first shape only and does not consider the other figures.

    B. Student calculates the perimeter instead of the area of the rectangle and miscalculates the area for the other shapes.

    C. Student miscalculates the area of the first two figures and determines that the trapezoid is the only figure that could generate the data.

    D. Correct. Student calculates the areas of all three shapes and determines that only the first and third shapes have areas of 12 square units.

    E. Student calculates the areas for the first and third shapes and the perimeter for the second shape. Based on these calculations, student determines that all three shapes could generate the data.

9.   Algebra 2 Module 3 Question 2

   A. Student selects a histogram that is skewed right, assuming that most of the values will be close to the lower end of the range.

   B. Student selects a histogram that is uniform, assuming that, since the values are randomly selected, they will be equally spread throughout the range.

   C. Correct. Student selects a histogram that is skewed left, recognizing that the values on the upper end of the range are more likely to be selected. When $1 \leq x \leq 3$, with the exception of $x = 2$, each y-value $1 \leq y < 4$ occurs twice. When $0 \leq x < 1$, each y-value $-8 \leq y < 1$ occurs once thus the graph will be skewed to the larger y-values and the median will be greater than 1. The frequency will also increase as the maximum y-value is approached.

   D. Student selects a histogram that is bi-modal, assuming that the values on the ends of the range are more likely to be selected than values in the middle of the range.

   E. Student selects a histogram that has its mode close to the middle of the range, assuming that the values in the middle of the range are more likely to be selected than values on the ends of the range.

Introduction to the NMSI Mathematics
Free Response Questions

The National Math and Science Initiative free response questions are modeled after free response questions on the AP* Calculus and Statistics exams. The questions are assigned a course-level designation based on an accelerated program that enables students to take college-level courses in high school, using a faster pace to compress content. In this sequence, Grades 6, 7, 8, and Algebra 1 are compacted into three courses. Grade 6 includes all of the Grade 6 content and some of the content from Grade 7, Grade 7 contains the remainder of the Grade 7 content and some of the content from Grade 8, and Algebra 1 includes the remainder of the content from Grade 8 and all of the Algebra 1 content.

The free response rubric is a guide to assist the reader, not a detailed solution to the question. Sometimes a method is outlined in the rubric, but another more efficient method may work as well. A student's correct solution may earn all of the points to be awarded for a particular part of the question, even though the approach does not match the one shown in the rubric. The rubric shows "a way" to work the problem, not "the way" to work the problem.

When scoring the free response questions, teachers should practice "reading with" a student's error. This statement means that the student is penalized for the error when it first occurs, but the reader then follows the student's process for full credit in subsequent parts of the question, even when the student continues to use the results of the earlier error. For the free response, the reader should be in the mindset of awarding points, not taking them away. Students start at 0 and can earn up to 9 points rather than starting at 9 points and losing points.

Student directions for the free response questions include the following:
- All work for a given part of a question must be shown in the space provided.
- Answers do not need to be simplified completely; however, when calculating approximate answers, do not round intermediate values. Your final answers should be accurate to three places after the decimal point.
- Questions that contain units require units in the answers.
- The setup for all mathematical computations and equations is required using mathematical notation rather than calculator syntax. Intermediate calculations do not have to be shown when determining:
  > the answer to basic arithmetic computations;
  > the zeroes of a function;
  > the maximum/minimum of a function;
  > the intersection point between two functions;
  > a regression equation.
- Part A and B are given equal weight, but parts of a particular question are not necessarily given equal weight.
- During the timed portion for Part A, you may work only on Part A. A calculator may be used on Part A only.
- During the timed portion for Part B, in addition to working on the question in Part B, you may continue to work on Part A without a calculator.

Grade 7 2008 Free Response Question - Calculator Allowed

The city of Fort Worth, Texas is in Tarrant County. The map below shows the county as the square region and the city as the shaded region inside the square. Fort Worth data about the age of the residents is given in the box-and-whisker plot, and population data is included in the table.

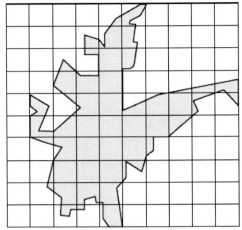

Map of the City of Fort Worth and Tarrant County

Ages of Fort Worth Residents in the Year 2000

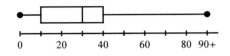

Fort Worth Census Data	
Year	Population
1990	447,619
2000	534,694

(a) Use the map of Fort Worth and Tarrant County to answer the following questions.

   (i) How many unit squares are totally shaded?

   (ii) Count the partially shaded squares. Add the number of partially shaded squares to the number of totally shaded squares. How many unit squares are either partially shaded or totally shaded?

   (iii) What percentage of the land in Tarrant County is within the city limits of Fort Worth? Use the average of parts (i) and (ii) and the total number of unit squares in Tarrant County to calculate the answer.

(b) Use the box-and-whisker plot and the table information for the year 2000 to answer the following questions.

    (i) What was the percentage of the people living in Fort Worth who were between the ages of 10 and 40? Write a sentence that includes the answer and provides a justification.

    (ii) How many people were between the ages of 10 and 40? Write a sentence that includes the answer and provides a justification.

    (iii) What was the approximate median age for the population? Write a sentence that includes the answer and provides a justification.

    (iv) Is a Fort Worth resident who is 95 years old an outlier in the age data? Write a sentence that includes the answer and provides a justification.

(c) The area of the city of Fort Worth is 292 square miles. What was the number of people per square mile in the year 1990? in the year 2000? Round the answers to the nearest whole number and include the units with the answers.

(d) The average rate of change in the number of people per square mile is the increase in the number of people per square mile divided by the increase in time. What is the average rate of change in the number of people per square mile from 1990 to 2000? Show the set up for the calculation. Round the answer to the nearest whole number and include the units with the answer.

Introduction to AP - Level Statistics Free Response Questions

The AP-Level Statistics free response questions are modeled after AP Statistics questions on the released exams. These questions incorporate many of the skills and concepts emphasized in this module as well as modeling the rigor and style of the AP Statistics exam.

When scoring solutions to these sample questions, teachers should practice using a "holistic" approach. A student who does not earn all the credit in one part of the problem can recoup the credit in another part of the problem. For special situations an incorrect approach carried out correctly can earn much of the credit for the question.

The scoring for the AP Statistics exam is different than for the AP Calculus exam. There are 4 points available on each free response question. Students are generally asked to answer 3 or 4 tasks each of which is awarded an E (essentially correct), P (partially correct), or I (incorrect) for their response. The combination of E's, P's, and I's is then awarded 4, 3, 2, 1, or 0 points.

The free response rubric is a guide to assist the reader, not a detailed solution to the question. A student's correct solution may earn all the credit awarded in a particular part of the question, even though the approach does not match the one shown in the rubric. The rubric shows "a way" to work the problem, not "the way" to work the problem. For the free response a reader should be in the mindset of awarding credit not taking it away.

AP - Level Statistics Question 1

In order to award scholarships to incoming freshmen, a university's science department developed an admissions exam for high school seniors. The graph below displays the scores of 40 seniors at the local school district's Science Magnet. Scores on this exam ranged from 6 to 67 points.

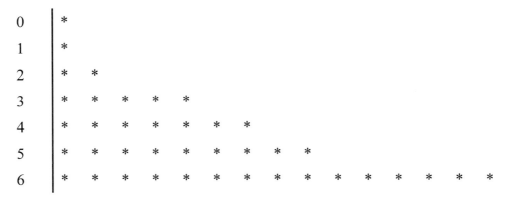

(a) Describe the shape of this distribution.

(b) The midrange is defined as $\dfrac{\text{maximum} + \text{minimum}}{2}$. Compute this value.

Is the midrange considered a measure of center or spread? Explain.

(c) The university wanted to report back to the high school that, overall, their students' performance on the admissions exam was high. Which summary statistic, the mean or the median, should the university use to report that the overall performance on the admissions exam was high? Explain.

AP - Level Statistics Question 2

The following table represents the results of the 2008 NCAA Midwest Regional men's and women's shot put finals. These distances are given in meters.

	Men	Women
Mean	17.07	15.34
Median	17.03	15.23
Minimum	15.28	13.92
Maximum	18.72	17.32
Lower quartile	16.14	14.70
Upper quartile	17.92	15.84

(a) Draw boxplots for the shot put distances for men and women. Use the same scale for both plots.

(b) Write several sentences to compare the variability of the two distributions.

(c) Write a few sentences describing the men's and women's performances in this event for the college newsletter.

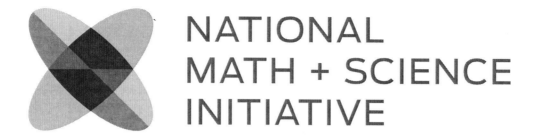

NATIONAL
MATH + SCIENCE
INITIATIVE

Appendix

NATIONAL
MATH + SCIENCE
INITIATIVE

This page is intentionally left blank.

www.nms.org

Standards for Mathematical Practice

MP.1 - Make sense of problems and persevere in solving them.
Mathematically proficient students:
- start by explaining to themselves the meaning of a problem and looking for entry points to its solution.
- analyze givens, constraints, relationships, and goals.
- make conjectures about the form and meaning of the solution and plan a solution pathway rather than simply jumping into a solution attempt.
- consider analogous problems, and try special cases and simpler forms of the original problem in order to gain insight into its solution.
- monitor and evaluate their progress and change course if necessary.
- Older students might, depending on the context of the problem,
  - transform algebraic expressions or change the viewing window on their graphing calculator to get the information they need,
  - explain correspondences between equations, verbal descriptions, tables, and graphs,
  - draw diagrams of important features and relationships, graph data, and search for regularity or trends.
- Younger students might:
  - rely on using concrete objects or pictures to help conceptualize and solve a problem.
- check their answers to problems using a different method, and they continually ask themselves, "Does this make sense?"
- understand the approaches of others to solving complex problems and identify correspondences between different approaches.

In assessments, the question:
- is designed to take a typical student a long time to solve.
- leads to a more difficult problem.
- requires a large number of routine and fairly easy steps.
- contains several "givens."
- the statement of the problem itself is designed not to allow for jumping in and working the problem immediately.
- posed using abstract statements that must be parsed carefully before they make sense.
- require students to construct their own solution pathway rather than to follow a provided one.
- may be unscaffolded so that a multi-step strategy must be autonomously devised by the student.
- involve ideas that are currently at the forefront of the student's developing mathematical knowledge in a word problem.

MP.2 - Reason abstractly and quantitatively.

Mathematically proficient students:

- make sense of quantities and their relationships in problem situations.

- bring two complementary abilities to bear on problems involving quantitative relationships:

    o the ability to *decontextualize*—to abstract a given situation and represent it symbolically and manipulate the representing symbols as if they have a life of their own, without necessarily attending to their referents—and

    o the ability to *contextualize*, to pause as needed during the manipulation process in order to probe into the referents for the symbols involved.

- use quantitative reasoning that entails habits of creating a coherent representation of the problem at hand:

    o considering the units involved;

    o attending to the meaning of quantities, not just how to compute them; and

    o knowing and flexibly using different properties of operations and objects.

In assessment, the question is designed to:

- be contextual so that the student can gain insight into the problem by relating the algebraic form of an answer or intermediate step to the given context.

- require the use symbolic calculations to generalize a situation and draw conclusions from those calculations.

MP.3 - Construct viable arguments and critique the reasoning of others.
Mathematically proficient students:

- understand and use stated assumptions, definitions, and previously established results in constructing arguments.

- make conjectures and build a logical progression of statements to explore the truth of their conjectures.

- analyze situations by breaking them into cases, and can recognize and use counterexamples.

- justify their conclusions, communicate them to others, and respond to the arguments of others.

- reason inductively about data, making plausible arguments that take into account the context from which the data arose.

- compare the effectiveness of two plausible arguments, distinguish correct logic or reasoning from that which is flawed, and – if there is a flaw in an argument – explain what it is.
  - Elementary students can construct arguments using concrete referents such as objects, drawings, diagrams, and actions. Such arguments can make sense and be correct, even though they are not generalized or made formal until later grades.
  - Later, students learn to determine domains to which an argument applies.

- listen to or read the arguments of others, decide whether they make sense, and ask useful questions to clarify or improve the arguments.

In assessments, require students to:

- base explanations/reasoning on concrete referents such as diagrams (whether provided in the prompt or constructed by the student).

- construct, autonomously, chains of reasoning that will justify or refute propositions or conjectures.

- determine conditions under which an argument does and does not apply.

- distinguish correct explanations/reasoning from that which is flawed, and – if there is a flaw in the argument – explain what it is.

- provide informal justifications.

- use of diagrams, words, and/or equations to solve.

- reason about key grade-level mathematics.

- apply rigorous deductive proof based on clearly stated axioms.

- state logical assumptions being used.

- test propositions or conjectures with specific examples.

- apply a series of logical and well-motivated steps with precise language and terms.

MP.4 - Model with mathematics.

Mathematically proficient students:

- apply the mathematics they know to solve problems arising in everyday life, society, and the workplace.
  - In early grades, this might be as simple as writing an addition equation to describe a situation.
  - In middle grades, a student might apply proportional reasoning to plan a school event or analyze a problem in the community.
  - By high school, a student might use geometry to solve a design problem or use a function to describe how one quantity of interest depends on another.
- apply what they know are comfortable making assumptions and approximations to simplify a complicated situation, realizing that these may need revision later.
- identify important quantities in a practical situation and map their relationships using such tools as diagrams, two-way tables, graphs, flowcharts and formulas.
- analyze those relationships mathematically to draw conclusions.
- routinely interpret their mathematical results in the context of the situation and reflect on whether the results make sense, possibly improving the model if it has not served its purpose.

In assessments, require students to:

- apply a known technique from pure mathematics to a real-world situation in which the technique yields valuable results even though it is not obviously applicable in a strict mathematical sense.
- execute some or all of the modeling cycle: formulate, compute, interpret, validate, and report.
- select from a data source, analyze the data and draw reasonable conclusions from it, often resulting in an evaluation or recommendation.
- use reasonable estimates of known quantities in a chain of reasoning that yields an estimate of an unknown quantity.
- make assumptions and simplifications.
- select from the data at hand or estimate data that are missing.
- use reasonable estimates of known quantities in a chain of reasoning that yields an estimate of an unknown quantity.

MP.5 - Use appropriate tools strategically.

Mathematically proficient students:

- consider the available tools when solving a mathematical problem (these tools might include pencil and paper, concrete models, a ruler, a protractor, a calculator, a spreadsheet, a computer algebra system, a statistical package, or dynamic geometry software).

- are sufficiently familiar with tools appropriate for their grade or course to make sound decisions about when each of these tools might be helpful, recognizing both the insight to be gained and their limitations.

- High school students:

  - analyze graphs of functions and solutions generated using a graphing calculator.

  - detect possible errors by strategically using estimation and other mathematical knowledge.

  - when making mathematical models, know that technology can enable them to visualize the results of varying assumptions, explore consequences, and compare predictions with data.

- identify relevant external mathematical resources, such as digital content located on a website, and use them to pose or solve problems.

- use technological tools to explore and deepen their understanding of concepts.

In assessments, questions involve

- making the coordinate plane essential for solving the problem, yet no direction is given to the student to use coordinates.

- creating circumstances for poor use or misuse of tools.

- posing questions that are fairly easy to solve or to answer correctly if a diagram is drawn first, but very hard to solve or to answer correctly if a diagram is not drawn, yet no direction is given to draw a diagram.

- using formulas or conversions where there is no prompting to use them.

- data sets of 15-30 numbers.

- using a calculator to test conjectures with many specific cases.

- substituting messy numerical values into a complicated expression and find the numerical result.

MP.6 - Attend to precision.
Mathematically proficient students:
- try to communicate precisely to others.
- try to use clear definitions in discussion with others and in their own reasoning.
- state the meaning of the symbols they choose, including using the equal sign consistently and appropriately.
- are careful about specifying units of measure and labeling axes to clarify the correspondence with quantities in a problem.
- calculate accurately and efficiently, express numerical answers with a degree of precision appropriate for the problem context.
  - In the elementary grades, students give carefully formulated explanations to each other.
  - By the time they reach high school, students have learned to examine claims and make explicit use of definitions.

In assessments, require students to:
- use reasoned solving of equations, such as those in which extraneous solutions are likely to be found and must be discarded.
- solve algebraic word problems in which success depends on carefully defining variables.
- present solutions to multi-step problems in the form of valid chains of reasoning, using symbols such as equal signs appropriately.

MP.7 - Look for and make use of structure.
Mathematically proficient students:

- look closely to discern a pattern or structure.
  - Young students, for example, might notice that three and seven more is the same amount as seven and three more, or they may sort a collection of shapes according to how many sides the shapes have.
  - Later, students will see 7×8 equals the well-remembered $7 \times 5 + 7 \times 3$, in preparation for learning about the distributive property.
  - In the expression $x^2 + 9x + 14$, older students can see the 14 as 2×7 and the 9 as $2 + 7$.
  - They recognize the significance of an existing line in a geometric figure and can use the strategy of drawing an auxiliary line for solving problems.
- step back for an overview and shift perspective.
- see complicated things, such as some algebraic expressions, as single objects or as being composed of several objects. For example, they can see $5 - 3(x - y)^2$ as 5 minus a positive number times a square and use that to realize that its value cannot be more than 5 for any real numbers x and y.

In assessments, questions:

- can be solved by analyzing parts of figures in relation to one another.
- can be solved by introducing auxiliary lines into a figure.
- reward seeing structure in an algebraic expression and using the structure to rewrite it for a purpose.
- reward or require deferring calculation steps until one sees the overall structure.
- assess how aware students are of how concepts link together and why mathematical procedures work in the way that they do.

MP.8 - Look for and express regularity in repeated reasoning.
Mathematically proficient students:
- notice if calculations are repeated, and look both for general methods and for shortcuts.
    - Upper elementary students might notice when dividing 25 by 11 that they are repeating the same calculations over and over again, and conclude they have a repeating decimal.
    - By paying attention to the calculation of slope as they repeatedly check whether points are on the line through $(1, 2)$ with slope 3, middle school students might abstract the equation $(y - 2)/(x - 1) = 3$.
    - Noticing the regularity in the way terms cancel when expanding $(x - 1)(x + 1)$, $(x - 1)(x^2 + x + 1)$, and $(x - 1)(x^3 + x^2 + x + 1)$ might lead them to the general formula for the sum of a geometric series.
- maintain oversight of the process, while attending to the details.
- continually evaluate the reasonableness of their intermediate results.

In assessments, questions require:
- repeating calculations to lead to the articulation of a conjecture.
- working repetitively with numerical examples leading without prompting to the writing of equations or functions that describe modeling situations.
- recognizing that tedious and repetitive calculation can be made shorter by observing regularity in the repeated steps.
- answers like "multiplying by any number and then dividing by the same number gets you back to where you started."
- using recursive definitions of functions.
- using patterns to shed light on the addition table, the times table, the properties of operations, the relationship between addition and subtraction or multiplication and division, and the place value system.

Additional Graphs and Materials

Viewing and Describing Data - Definitions

Bar graph

A bar graph is a graphical display of categorical data made up of vertical or horizontal bars with a gap between the bars. The bars are the same width and each one represents a particular category. The length of each bar is proportional to the counts in the category it represents.

Bi-modal

A set of data can be called bimodal if it has two modes: however, in statistics bimodal is used to describe the shape of the data. A graph is bimodal if the distribution has two apparent peaks.

Box-and-whisker plot (boxplot)

A boxplot is a way of summarizing a set of data and is a type of graph which is used to show the shape of the distribution, the median, and the variability. The graph displays the five-number summary which includes the maximum and minimum values, the lower and upper quartiles, and the median.

A boxplot is especially helpful for indicating whether a distribution is skewed and whether there are any unusual observations (outliers) in the data set. Boxplots are useful when there are a large number of observations or when two or more data sets are being compared.

Categorical data

Categorical variables represent types of data which can be sorted into unique groups so that every value belongs to one and only one category. Examples of categorical variables are colors of cars, states of residence, countries of birth, and zip codes.

Center

The center is the point in the distribution where approximately half of the values lie to the left and approximately half of the values lie to the right.

Deviation

Deviation is the difference between the value of a data point and arithmetic mean of the data. This value is determined by subtracting the mean from the data point. When the deviation is positive, the data point is greater than the mean. When the deviation is negative, the data point is less than the mean.

Dotplot (Line plot)

A dotplot represents each piece of data as a dot positioned along a scale or axis. The scale can be either horizontal or vertical. The horizontal position is more common. Each dot represents a single individual or a fixed number of individuals. A dotplot can also detect any unusual observations (outliers), or any gaps in the data set.

Empirical rule

The empirical rule states that in a Normal Model about 68% of the values fall within one standard deviation of the mean, approximately 95% of the values fall within two standard deviations from the mean, and about 99.7% fall within three standard deviations from the mean. This implies that approximately all of the values fall within three standard deviations of the mean when the data follows a normal distribution.

Five-number summary

A 5-number summary consists of 5 values: the maximum and minimum values, the lower and upper quartiles, and the median. A 5-number summary is used to describe data and to create a box-and-whisker plot.

Gaps and clusters

Some distributions are concentrated about several values with space between those concentrations. The concentrations are called clusters. Clusters occur when the data has many numbers that are very close together. Large spaces between data points or clusters are called gaps. Gaps contain NO members of the distribution.

Graphical displays of categorical data

Pie charts and bar charts are used to represent the distribution of the categorical data. With a bar chart, categorical variables are usually defined by the categories displayed on the x-axis and the counts on the y-axis.

Graphical displays of quantitative data

Boxplots, histograms, stemplots, and dotplots are basic tools for viewing quantitative data.

Histogram

A histogram is a graphical display of a data set that shows the data set's distribution. It divides the data into classes (bins), uses adjacent bars, and gives the frequency for each class. Histograms are particularly useful for summarizing large data sets. The histogram is only appropriate for quantitative data and is generally used when dealing with large data sets. A histogram can also help detect any unusual observations (outliers), or any gaps in the data set.

IQR

The interquartile range is a measure of the spread within a data set between the upper and lower quartiles and is calculated by taking the difference of these values. For example:

Data	2 3 4 5 6 6 6 7 7 8 9
Upper quartile	7
Lower quartile	4
IQR	7 - 4 = 3

The IQR represents the width of an interval which contains the middle 50% of the data. It is smaller than the range and its value is less affected by outliers.

Median

The median is a measure of center that divides a population or sample into two equal parts. Arrange the data in either descending or ascending order to determine the value. The median is a good descriptive measure of the center when the data is skewed or contains outliers.

Mean

The arithmetic mean of a set of data is the quantity commonly called the mean or the average and is a measure of center. It may not appear representative of the central region for skewed data sets. The value of the mean depends equally on all of the data which may include outliers. It is especially useful as being representative of symmetrically distributed data.

Mean Absolute Deviation

The mean absolute deviation measures the average distance between the arithmetic mean of the data and a data point.

Mode

The mode of a set of data is the data value that occurs most often. If a data set contains multiple values with the same maximum frequency, then the data set has multiple modes. For instance, in a set of test scores if 5 students earn an 85 and 5 students earn a 90 and 5 is the highest frequency, then both 85 and 90 are modes.

Modified boxplot

A modified boxplot is a boxplot that uses a symbol (sometimes an asterisk) to show outliers.

Non-resistant to Outliers

When the value of a summary statistic is greatly affected by an unusually large or unusually small observation (outlier), the value is considered to be non-resistant to outliers. The mean is an example of a non-resistant measure of center.

Normal Distribution

Normal distributions are "bell-shaped" curves with unimodal and symmetrical shapes. The mean is used as a measure of center and standard deviation as the measure of variability.

Outliers

An outlier is a data value which is an unusually large or an unusually small value compared to the others. An outlier might be the result of an error in measurement or it might be a value that needs further investigation. In either case, these values may distort the interpretation of the data and have undue influence on many summary statistics, such as the mean. Outliers should not routinely be removed from a data set without further justification. An outlier is often defined as a data point that is more than $1.5 \times IQR$ below the first quartile or one that is more than $1.5 \times IQR$ above the third quartile.

Quantitative data

Data which are recorded in numbers for which arithmetic operations are appropriate are quantitative. Quantitative data often have measurement units that tell how a quantitative value has been recorded. Examples of quantitative data include age, length, and the number of dots showing on a die. Zip codes and numbers on a football player's uniform are not quantitative variables.

Quartiles

Quartiles are values that divide a sample of data into four groups containing equal numbers of observations, if possible. A data set has three quartiles; the upper quartile, Q_3, the lower quartile, Q_1, and the second quartile, the median. The lower quartile (25th percentile) is the data value a quarter of the way up through the ordered data set; the upper quartile (75th percentile) is the data value a quarter of the way down through the ordered data set.

Example

Data	6 47 49 15 43 41 7 39 43 41 36
Ordered Data	6 7 15 36 39 41 41 43 43 47 49
Median	41
Upper quartile	43
Lower quartile	15

Range

The range is the difference between the largest and the smallest observed value of quantitative data and measures the spread of the distribution. The range of a data set is greatly influenced by the presence of just one unusually large or unusually small value in the sample.

Resistant to Outliers

When the value of a measure of center or spread is not affected by an unusually large or small observation, the value is considered to be resistant to outliers. The median is an example of a measure of center which is resistant to outliers.

Shape

One very important characteristic of a distribution is its shape. Shape is determined by high points (modes), uniformity, symmetry, or skewed distributions.

Skewed

A distribution is skewed if the data is not symmetric and stretches further out on one side. Values on one side of the distribution tend to be further from the "middle" than values on the other side. When a graphical display is skewed "right", the mean will be larger than the median. When a graphical display is skewed "left", the median will be larger than the mean. When the longer "tail" of the data is on the right, the data is described as skewed right.

Spread

Spread provides information about the variability of the data. Measures of spread include range and interquartile range.

Standard Deviation

Standard deviation is a measure of spread (variability) that describes the average or typical distance a data point is from the mean. When the mean is reported as the measure of center, the standard deviation is used to describe variability.

Stem-and-leaf plot

A stem-and-leaf plot is a way of summarizing a set of quantitative data measured on an interval scale. It is often used in exploratory data analysis to illustrate the major features of the distribution of the data. A stem-and-leaf plot is similar to a histogram but is usually a more informative display for relatively small data sets (<100 data points). It provides a table as well as a picture of the data and from it we can readily determine the median, mode, and range. More than one data set can be compared by using multiple stem-and-leaf plots. By using a back-to-back stem-and-leaf plot, the same characteristics in two different groups can be compared.

Symmetrical

When data is distributed in such a way that the two halves on either side of the center have approximately the same shape, the distribution is symmetric. When a graphical display is symmetric, the mean and median will be approximately equal.

Univariate data

Data that consists of observations on a single variable is called univariate data. The data set may be either categorical or quantitative.

Viewing and Describing Data - Activity

Without consulting anyone else, examine the list and circle the terms you know. Count the number of circled terms and write your number on a sticky note. Add your sticky note to the entire group's graphical display. Once you have completed this task, you may discuss the terms with your group.

Bar graph	Mode
Bi-modal	Modified boxplot
Box-and-whisker plot (Boxplot)	Non-resistant to outliers
Categorical data	Normal Distribution
Center	Outliers
Deviation	Quantitative data
Dotplot (Line plot)	Quartiles
Empirical Rule	Range
Five-number summary	Resistant to outliers
Gaps and clusters	Shape
Graphical displays of categorical data	Skewed
Graphical displays of quantitative data	Spread
Histogram	Standard Deviation
IQR	Stem-and-leaf plot
Median	Symmetrical
Mean	Univariate Data
Mean Absolute Deviation	

Viewing and Describing Data

Words teachers know

Viewing and Describing Data Boxplot

Words teachers know

Viewing and Describing Data Stemplots

Words teachers know	Words teachers recognize	Words teachers feel they could teach

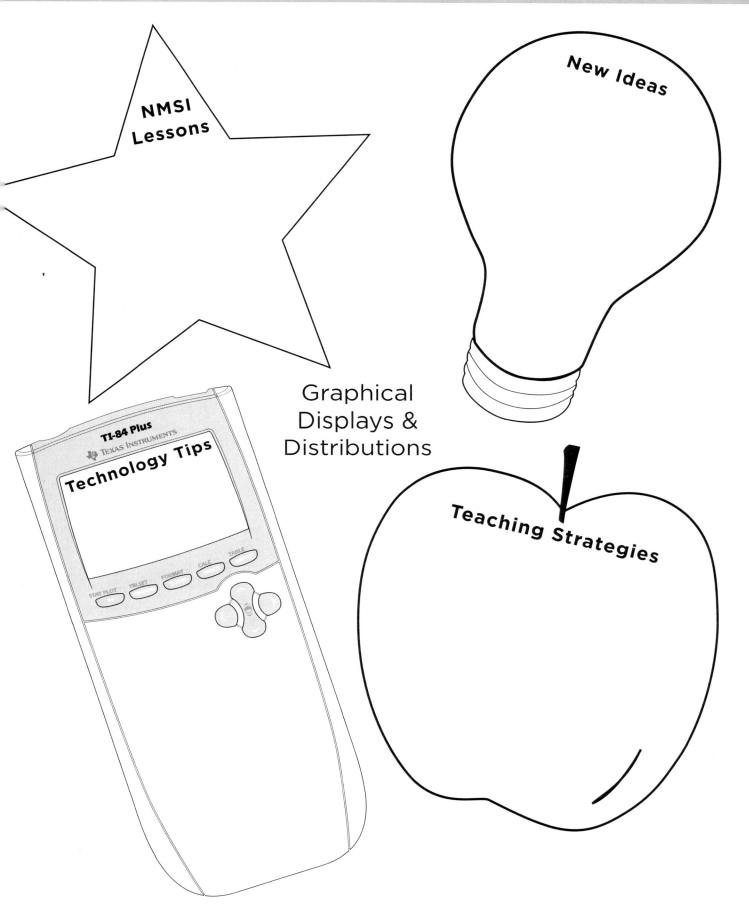

NMSI
Lessons

New Ideas

Graphical
Displays &
Distributions

TI-84 Plus
TEXAS INSTRUMENTS
Technology Tips

Teaching Strategies

STAT PLOT   TBLSET   FORMAT   CALC   TABLE

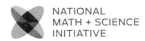

This page is intentionally left blank.

www.nms.org